Robert Fulton

BOY CRAFTSMAN

Avyx

Illustrated by Robert Patterson

Cover art by Drew Thurston

Robert Fulton

BOY CRAFTSMAN

by Marguerite Henry

Published by Avyx, Inc., 2008, 2010

ISBN: 978-1-887840-25-5

Avyx, Inc.
8032 S. Grant Way
Littleton, CO 80122
www.avyx.com
(303) 483-0140

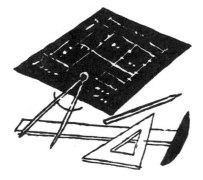

To

Roberta Sutton

Illustrations

Full pages

Numerous smaller illustrations

Contents

Bob and the Gunsmith

HERE IT was October in this year 1773. Yet the noonday sun beating down on Lancaster, Pennsylvania, was almost as warm as in mid-July. Yet the dry leaves, in shades of red, brown, and yellow, showed that it was fall.

Seven-year-old Bob Fulton hurried up the runway of the gunsmith's shop. Then he stopped short. He liked to see what kind of work was going on before he entered.

He looked very small in the wide-open doorway. But he looked determined, too. It was almost as if he were the gunsmith and this his shop. He wished it belonged to him.

The afternoon would be fun, he thought. The shop was busy. A mare, tied to the hitching post, stamped and pawed the ground as she waited her turn. Inside, a peddler of tinware snored in the chair by the door. His little stock of pans and kettles was heaped in front of him.

The ox cage was occupied, too. It held a huge brown and white ox. He was strapped into a sling which hung down from the ceiling. The creature looked worried and uncomfortable. He seemed to know that soon he would be hoisted into the air.

Funny, Bob thought, that an ox can't stand on three feet while the fourth is being shod!

He was glad that he was not so heavy as an ox. It would be clumsy to hang from the rafters while his mother or sisters put on his shoes!

He laughed to himself. Then suddenly he thought of the iron candlestick. Today was his mother's birthday, and he must finish it.

He walked quickly to the peg where a small cowhide apron hung. As he slipped it over his head, he noticed that the newness was beginning to wear off. There were actually a few darkish spots of axle grease on it. Soon it would look like the gunsmith's except for the size.

The gunsmith was busy selecting a piece of iron. He had not heard the boy's light footsteps.

"I'm here, Mr. Messersmith!" Bob shouted.

Now the gunsmith turned around. His smile widened until it showed the dark hole where two of his back teeth were missing.

"So you be!" he chuckled. "And just in time. What with bullets to cast and new muskets to make, I need a sharp lad to give me a hand. But Jack in the ox cage and the mare at the hitching post need shoes first."

"Yes, sir!" replied Bob. "You need a strong boy to pump the bellows. Your fire is not hot enough to get all this work done."

Mr. Messersmith laughed, a booming noisy laugh that seemed part of the forge and the fire. "For a lad of seven," he said, "you have more sense than a dozen full-grown men."

Bob flew around to the back of the chimney and built himself a footstool of bricks. Then standing on the bricks, he reached for the long wooden handle that worked the bellows. Up and down, up and down he pumped. There was a great wheezy noise, louder than that made by the snoring peddler.

As he pumped he glanced down at his muscles. Each day he hoped they would swell up big, like the gunsmith's. At times he was sure they were getting bigger.

Now he peered around the chimney. Mr. Messersmith seemed pleased. He was lifting the red-hot iron out of the coals. And almost at once came the great ringing sound of the hammer on the anvil.

When Bob stepped down off the bricks, he noticed that the dirt floor needed sweeping. Broken nails, scraps of iron, and hoof parings were scattered everywhere.

With long strokes of the broom, he kept time to the wonderful music of the anvil. Even when he swept around the ox cage, he did not miss a beat. He loved rhythm.

At last the oxshoes were shaped, and the gunsmith was plunging them into cold water. They made a loud hissing sound. At the exact moment when the hissing began, the peddler jumped into the air.

"A snake!" he cried, his eyes bulging with terror. And in his excitement he stumbled over his tinware and sprawled headlong. Johnnycake pans, cooky cutters, dippers, and mugs rattled and rolled to the far corner of the shop.

"It's no snake you hear," roared the gunsmith, slapping his thigh. "It's Jack's shoes hissing."

The peddler could take a joke on himself. He laughed until the buttons on his waistcoat rose up and down like ducks riding the waves.

Bob, too, was doubled in laughter. It was all he could do to gather up the peddler's stock.

"Happens you're too busy to give me a hand with Jack?" Mr. Messersmith asked Bob with a twinkle in his eye. He knew that this was Bob's favorite task.

Quick as a flash the boy found the last cooky cutter. Then, feeling very important, he took hold of the crank that turned the wheel in the loft. *Squeak, squeak* sounded the wheel. Slowly, slowly it turned. The rope was moving. And the great ox in his leather sling was lifted off his tiny feet. Helpless as a kitten, he hung swaying in the air.

"Not every lad can lift an ox!" winked the gunsmith. "There's probably not another lad in Lancaster who's as strong as an ox."

Bob Fulton stood with his feet braced far apart, his hands on his hips. He felt stronger than an ox.

FORGING A CANDLESTICK

On most days Bob liked to watch the gunsmith fix oxshoes. Two tiny shoes to each cloven hoof. But today he had more important business.

From the bench by the window he took a bar of iron. It was about a foot long, and already it resembled a candlestick.

"One more heating and shaping and no queen could have a finer gift!" nodded Mr. Messersmith. "But before candlelighting time I'm going to need a good supply of nails."

Bob tried not to show his disappointment. Anxiously he raised his eyes to the sun. It still rode high in the sky. There might be time to shape the nails and finish the candlestick, too.

He shoved a half-dozen rods into the glowing mouth of the forge. They were no bigger than rats' tails and heated quickly. In just a little while he was beating them out into nails with funny square heads.

When he had one hundred nails in the keg, he felt the gunsmith's hand on his shoulder.

"I've set your candlestick in the forge, lad," he said kindly. "You've done enough work."

Bob's small hands trembled with excitement. He picked up the tongs. Carefully he moved the slender piece of iron into the heart of the fire. Now Mr. Messersmith was actually working the bellows for him! The boy looked up and smiled. The gunsmith smiled back. Bob thought him the handsomest man in the world. Even the dark hole where there should have been teeth looked friendly and interesting. What did it matter if a boy had no father so long as he had a friend like the gunsmith!

"I judge the iron to be right, sir!" shouted Bob above the noise.

The gunsmith stopped pumping the bellows.

Bob worked quickly now. He swung the glowing metal to the anvil. With the tongs in his left hand, he kept turning it. All the while he tapped and shaped it with a light hammer.

PENNIES FROM THE GUNSMITH

The sun was low in the heavens when Bob slipped off his leather apron. How wonderfully dirty it looked! There were charcoal smudges all over it. What was more, it bellied out as if he were still inside it!

Bob grinned in satisfaction. In no time at all he would be grown up! It would be fine to earn money. He would buy his mother a farm, and for his sisters he would choose bonnets and caraway cakes.

He might even give little Abraham a coin now and then— although sometimes Abraham could be a nuisance, leaving his chores for Bob to do.

The shop was empty now. The peddler and his newly shod ox were gone. Only the gunsmith worked on.

"It's a pity we've no paper to wrap so fine a candlestick," he said. "In the whole colony of Pennsylvania I've never seen a finer piece."

"My mother won't mind about the wrapping, sir. But before I go," he added, "I've news to tell you."

"News?"

"Yes, sir. This night my mother gives me my last schooling. Tomorrow I go to Master Caleb Johnson's school. I may be late getting here."

"This is news indeed!" Mr. Messersmith stroked his beard thoughtfully. Then he reached into the pocket under his apron and produced two shiny pennies.

"These are for you," he said proudly. "They will buy one penny's worth of vermilion coloring and one penny's worth of copperas, and you can make red and black ink for school."

Two whole pennies for his own! He put them in the little cup of the candlestick and clamped his hand over them for safekeeping.

"Oh, thank you, sir! Mother will know how to make the ink."

"Happens I'd always wanted to letter with black ink and with red," the gunsmith added. "Now I'll enjoy knowing I bought the ink so you could write like a gentleman."

The gunsmith held out his hand. Bob put his little one inside the great horny warmth of the master's. He felt it close around with a clasp so strong it made him blink. He had never shaken hands man-to-man before. His heart grew warm, like the fire when the bellows breathed on it. It was fun to be big!

Gathering about the Board

BOB SKIPPED along the dirt road. Soon he came to a shop where there was a little window with a shelf outside. A wooden sign hung above the window. It pictured a small bowl with a kind of spoon inside — the mortar and pestle, sign of the chemist's shop.

Bob tapped on the open shutters.

A moonfaced man poked his head out.

"Why, bless me if it isn't Bob Fulton!" The man smiled. "And what are you making now?"

"Ink," replied Bob as he put his two pennies on the shelf. "I need one penny's worth of copperas, and one penny's worth of vermilion."

The man disappeared for a moment. When he came back, he handed two small packages out the window. "Here you are, lad," he said. "And the best there is."

Bob felt very happy as he headed for home. The candlestick, still warm, was hidden under his jacket. And the packages of coloring matter crackled in his pocket as he walked.

A cool wind was beginning to stir. It made the weather vanes on houses and barns turn sharply. It sent autumn leaves flying down the lane. Pigs ran snorting and squealing under fences. Dogs turned in at their own gateways. All living creatures seemed to be going home.

Even the horses needed no urging. The coaches of the rich and the carts of the poor whirled over the rough roads.

Suddenly Bob caught sight of the broad black hat and the black coat of the schoolmaster. How sober and frightening he looked!

Bob slowed to a walk. He stepped aside and made room for the schoolmaster to pass.

The schoolmaster did not so much as glance at his new pupil. He hurried on, his coattails trailing out behind him, like the forked tail of a swallow.

Bob shivered. He felt suddenly cold and forlorn. And he was not sure that he cared about going to school after all.

The village clock struck five as Bob pulled the string of his door latch. The next moment he felt the cozy warmth of the kitchen.

"Mother!" he called. "Surprise! Surprise! Surprise!"

Mrs. Fulton set down the bag of Indian meal she was holding. Peggy and Belle, his older sisters, dropped the yarn they were winding. Even little Polly and Abraham stopped chasing Matilda, the cat. They all gathered about Bob as he laid the candlestick in his mother's hands.

Mrs. Fulton ran her fingers down the slender iron stem. She felt the deep saucers made to catch the dripping wax. Then she turned the candlestick upside down and saw the careful lettering:

MOTHER
FROM
R.F.
1775

"What does it say?" piped Abraham and Polly at the same time.

"It says, 'Mother from R.F., 1773,'" read Peggy and Belle in chorus.

"Who is R.F.?" asked Abraham.

Bob lifted Abraham off his feet. "*I'm* R.F., goosy. Who did you think it was?"

Mrs. Fulton seemed to have a catch in her throat. "As long as I live," she said, "I shall always remember this birthday. But tell us, Bob, how did you manage to carve out the lettering?"

Bob flushed with pride. "I watched a red-headed woodpecker one day. He was using his beak as a chisel. He kept chipping away at the trunk of a tree. So I figured that with a real chisel I could chip out letters in the candlestick, and that's what I did."

"My little iron-pecker!" laughed Mrs. Fulton, burying her face in Bob's curly hair.

HASTY PUDDIN' TIME

Abraham stood on tiptoe and peeked into the pot of boiling water over the fire.

"Mamma!" he cried. "The water has stopped smiling. It is laughing out loud."

"Then it's hasty puddin' time!" nodded Mrs. Fulton. "Peggy, sprinkle the Indian meal into the water. Just a few grains at a time. Belle, add a snack of salt. Bob, you can stir it until it thickens. Don't let it burn."

"What can I do, Mamma?" asked Polly.

"What can *I* do?" asked Abraham.

"You may wash your hands and faces," said Mother. "And then you may set the table—the wooden bowls, the mugs for our tea, the salt box, and the spoons."

The kitchen hummed. Everyone was busy. Mrs. Fulton and the two older girls were everywhere at once. They were mixing sugar and nutmeg to sprinkle over the pudding. They were running to the milk cellar for a jug of rich milk. They were making tea from blackberry leaves. They were testing the thickness of the pudding so that it would be exactly right. They didn't want it to be too thick or too thin.

Even Matilda, the cat, was busy. She was polishing her whiskers.

Bob stirred and stirred the meal with his long pudding stick. He stood as far away from the hot fire as possible.

Mrs. Fulton laughed. "How is it, son, that you can stand the heat of the forge, but not the hearth fire?"

Stirring hasty pudding is girl's work, he thought. But he was saved the trouble of answering, for just then the pudding began to bubble.

"Mamma!" exclaimed Abraham. "Hasty puddin' is laughing."

"So it is, Abraham. Hang the kettle higher, Bob. Hasty puddin' need only cook slowly after it bubbles."

Mrs. Fulton took the pudding stick from Bob and handed him a flat wooden shovel.

"See what's in the oven, Bob. It will make up for all the stirring."

Carefully Bob opened the heavy oven door. And there, on the bricks, sat a plump pumpkin. It was toasted a golden brown, and it gave out a delicious spicy smell.

"Oh, oh!" shrieked all the children as they peeked into the oven.

Now Bob scooped his shovel underneath the pumpkin. Steadily he lifted it onto the platter which Peggy held out to him.

"Mm," breathed Bob as he sniffed the steaming fragrance.

THE NEW CANDLESTICK

"Gather about the board!" called Mrs. Fulton. "Come, Peggy, Belle, Bob, Polly, and Abraham! Now where has Belle gone?"

"I saw her go down cellar," Abraham spoke up. "Shall I go see if she is down there and tell her to hurry up?"

"Hush!" whispered Peggy. "It's a surprise."

Soon Belle appeared with the candle chest. She took out a candle that was different from the others. It was pale green.

Polly clapped her hands at sight of it. "See, Mamma!" she exclaimed. "Abraham and I gathered the bayberries. Peggy boiled them to get the wax. And Belle did the dipping. Isn't it beautiful, Mamma? And doesn't it smell fine?"

Mrs. Fulton looked at her little family with pride. "Of all mothers, I am the happiest," she said. "I'm sure there is no other mother in the world with such thoughtful children."

"Let's use the new candlestick!" shouted Abraham. "Let's put our beautiful green candle in the new candlestick!"

"Let's!" cried everyone, including Mrs. Fulton. All of them watched while Polly carefully placed the candle in the candlestick.

"Bob, will you light it for us?"

Bob held the candle to the glowing fire. It caught on slowly. Then he fitted it into the cup of the candlestick and gave it the place of honor next to the pumpkin.

Now, in the candlelight, six heads bent low. And six soft voices said:

> "Be present at our table, Lord;
> Be here and everywhere adored.
> Thy creatures bless, and grant that we
> May feast in paradise with Thee."

There was a moment of silence.

Then Mrs. Fulton took hold of the stem of the pumpkin and set the pumpkin's "hat" on the platter. Then all of them reached into the pumpkin to spoon up the roasted pumpkin meat. It was flavored with spices and honey, and it melted on the tongue.

When the pumpkin was nothing but a shell, Mrs. Fulton dished up the hasty pudding. Peggy and Belle hovered over the table like bees. They filled the mugs with steaming tea and sprinkled sugar and poured rich milk over the pudding. Then everyone ate with appetite.

Getting Ready
for School

"HARK!" MRS. FULTON held up her hand for silence. "The village clock strikes."

"One – two – three – four – five – six – seven," everyone counted aloud.

"It's only seven!" crowed Polly. "Bedtime is a whole hour away."

Bob seemed as pleased as Polly. He moved the table board nearer the firelight and brought out the two little packages of coloring matter.

"Is it sugar candy?" asked Abraham when he saw the green and red crystals.

"Nothing to eat, goosy. And a good thing. You're as stuffed as a puddin' bag."

"I'm a puddin' bag! I'm a puddin' bag!" sang Abraham, rubbing his fat round stomach and dancing around the table.

Quick as a rabbit Bob opened his packages. "I'm going to make ink," he said, his dark eyes shining with excitement.

Mrs. Fulton looked at the crystals in amazement. "Why, wherever did you get the money to buy copperas and vermilion?" she asked.

"Gunsmith gave me two pennies."

Suddenly the room was filled with excitement. The children crowded around Bob. Mrs. Fulton reached into the cubbyhole beside the chimney.

"See, Bob," she said, as she held up a tiny box. "It holds just enough ink powder for one batch of ink. Your father left it to you."

"He meant it for me, Mother? For me?"

Mrs. Fulton nodded. "He wanted you to write fair and clear. He wanted you to go to school and learn to do useful things."

Bob grew thoughtful as he added water to the powder and stirred it until it became a shiny black liquid.

"With ink powder won't I need the copperas?" he asked, trying to hide his disappointment. He did so want to use it.

"No, son. But one day you will find a use for it. You always do."

Mrs. Fulton went back to her spinning. "Now I'll give you the recipe for red ink while I spin. Polly and Abraham, keep your yarn away from the fire. Peggy and Belle, bring your knitting closer to the fire where you can see to work.

"Now then, Bob. Get the little earthenware jar. Into it put one yellow lump of gum arabic. This will make the coloring matter more permanent and improve the quality of the ink."

Bob's heart sang. He found the gum arabic on the wall dresser. He dropped a lump of it in the earthenware jar.

"Now some water?" he asked.

"Yes. Now some water. Just a mug full."

"Now the vermilion coloring matter?" he asked excitedly.

"Now the vermilion. And stir the mixture often, until the day after tomorrow."

"Until the day after tomorrow!" repeated Bob. "Why, it won't be ready in time for school."

"Nor does it matter, son. Your fine black ink is the most needed."

By now it was nearly bedtime. Abraham was tired of winding yarn. He stood up on his stool and began to juggle three ears of dried corn. All three ears hit the rafters.

Plop! Plop! Plop!

All three ears landed on the table board. One rolled over and upset the jar of black ink! Slowly the precious ink spread out in every direction.

There was a great stillness. The whole Fulton family was shocked by the disaster.

Bob turned white. He bit his lips. He wanted to hit little Abraham in the nose. He wanted to cry. But he did neither. Even now he could not help liking his frightened little brother. And *somehow* he would think of a way to make more ink.

THE GOOSEFOOT MAPLE

The first gray light was sifting through the shutters. Bob slid out of bed. Quietly he put on his old clothes. He tiptoed down the ladder steps. If only he could lift the latch without waking his mother!

For a moment he stood at the door. Matilda came rubbing against his legs, purring noisily.

"Sh, Matilda!" whispered Bob. "Must you rumble like a thunderstorm?"

When a wagon rattled down the lane, Bob lifted the latch and stole outdoors.

He took one deep breath and then raced for the swamp as if forty Indians were after him.

"It's got to be the bark of the goosefoot maple," he kept saying to himself. "The goosefoot maple that likes wet roots."

It was easy to single out the maple trees. Autumn had touched them off. Even in the woolly light of morning they were yellow and crimson.

Quickly Bob began stripping the bark from one tree. He hurried home with his arms full.

The house was still asleep. The fire was ashed over. The shutters still had their eyelids closed.

Bob tiptoed around the kitchen. He put the bark in the old black kettle over the fire. Next he poured nearly a bucket of water over it. Now he kindled the fire.

"A watched pot never boils," he said to himself. "I won't even look at it. I'll stir the red ink instead." So he stirred the red ink madly. Then he swept the hearth.

Now the water was beginning to sputter. It was laughing out loud. It was thickening. Why, it was turning a nice darkish brown! At last he could add the copperas.

Bob was so busy he did not hear his mother come into the kitchen.

"Bob Fulton!" she exclaimed. "You're making ink. Enough for the whole school!"

Bob grinned. "Do you think it will write?" he asked anxiously.

"We shall know very soon."

Now Mrs. Fulton tiptoed, too, so as not to waken the lively brood in the loft. She seemed as excited as Bob. She brought out a goose-quill pen and some coarse brown wrapping paper. Carefully she cut the wrapping paper into sheets about two feet square.

She folded one of the sheets two times. Then it was one-quarter of its original size. With a knife she slit open the bottom folds.

Next she folded one of these sheets in half. Then she folded it once again, until it was one-quarter of its original size. Now, with a snick-snurr, she slit open the bottom folds with a knife.

"Why, Mother!" exclaimed Bob. "It's like a book! How did you know how to do it? Are all books made like that? You've made eight little pages out of one sheet!"

"So I have."

"But aren't you ever going to try my ink?"

"Let patience grow in your garden," smiled Mrs. Fulton. "Suppose you fold four more sheets just like this."

Bob knew that his mother never asked him to do things without reason. So he folded and folded, and snick-snurr went the knife as he ripped open the bottom folds.

"Now slip one fold inside the other," called Mrs. Fulton, her head almost hidden in the cubbyhole beside the chimney.

Endless treasures seemed to be stored in that little cubbyhole. This time Mrs. Fulton found a small roll of wallpaper. Dim figures of girls and boys skated over the paper, like children in a dream. Skillfully Mrs. Fulton fitted the wallpaper around the folded pages to form a gay cover. Then she sewed cover and pages together.

Bob thought he could not hold his excitement another minute. Was she never going to try the ink? Maybe she would if he handed her the pen.

He went over to the huge pot of ink and dipped the pen. He offered it to his mother.

She took it as if she had wanted it that very moment. Then, in her fine hand, she wrote across the wallpaper cover:

*This Copybook
belongs to
Robert Fulton*

Bob caught his breath. "Why, it's beautiful!" he said softly. "The ink works. It actually works!" He laughed.

The ink had a curious color. Not quite brown nor black nor blue. It was a mixture of all three. But Bob had made it himself. And to him and his mother, no color could be more beautiful.

The Quaker School

BOB TURNED out of the gate. He had a queer feeling in his stomach. Yesterday he had wanted to go to school more than anything in the world. But today, somehow, home seemed very nice. He didn't want to leave it and face all those children at school.

Abraham and his sisters were still calling goodby. He looked around and saw them all waving to him from the doorway. His mother was there, too.

He wanted to wave back. But there was his lunch pail in one hand, and his inkhorn and copybook in the other.

He kept turning around and nodding until he stumbled over a tree root, and nearly upset his pail and dropped his book.

From then on, he walked straight ahead. The school bell would not ring for almost an hour; so he could take his time. Perhaps some round-about way would be pleasant.

He began to look about him. Up the hill he could see the new Swiss settler digging a long trench. He trudged up the hill to find out why.

The new settler was pleased to talk about his plans. "I, Hans Holzer," he said, "never went to school yet. But I can think and work. Look once. I dig ditches in the hills, and down comes the water. Soon Hans Holzer's land is rich."

Bob was eager with questions. How deep would Mr. Holzer have to dig? What would he plant? Why couldn't he build a little boat next? Wouldn't he save time if he used boats to ship his crops to market?

Hans Holzer was a good-natured man. He answered Bob's questions, one by one. Finally he pointed to Bob's Sabbath Day suit, and to his wooden pail and his inkhorn.

"Now," he laughed, "I, Hans Holzer, ask the questions. Where go you all dressed up when it is not First Day?"

Bob's eyes grew round. "To school!" he shouted in sudden alarm. "I'm going to be late to school!"

Running, stumbling down the hill, Bob arrived breathless at the school door.

It was closed.

He could not see into the windows, for they were made of paper. He looked about helplessly. There was not another child in sight. Only a rabbit bounding across the school grounds had stopped to stare at him.

With a timid heart, he set down his lunch pail and opened the door.

QUESTIONS AND ANSWERS

Bob heard a dozen goose-quill pens scratching. He saw a dozen heads bent over their copybooks. He saw the stern Quaker schoolmaster sitting behind his high desk in the center of the room reading a book.

Bob stepped just inside the door and waited.

At last the schoolmaster laid aside his book. He tapped sharply on the desk with a bundle of birch rods.

A dozen pens stopped scratching. A dozen pairs of eyes peered at Bob.

The schoolmaster rose. He took a key from his pocket and began winding his watch. It made a noisy grinding sound. He looked from his watch to Bob and back again.

Now he carefully took off his square spectacles. Slowly he put them in his spectacle case. He turned his eyes on Bob. They bulged like those of a frog.

"Tell the class thy name," he said in an icy voice which chilled the small boy.

"Robert Fulton," came the small reply.

"Speak up!"

"Yes, sir."

"Does thee have any learning?

"Yes, sir. My mother has taught me to read and write, but I wish to learn many things."

"If thee would learn, why does thee tarry along the way?"

"Oh, but I was learning only this morning."

"Indeed!" And the schoolmaster's black brows climbed halfway up his forehead. He tightened his grip on the birch rods. "And will thee tell us thy learning?"

"Yes, sir. Hans Holzer digs ditches in the hills and brings water to his fields. His fields will be rich."

"Enough chatter. Get to thy seat!" He pointed to an empty bench with his bundle of birch rods.

The morning dragged slowly by. The log bench grew harder each minute. The air in the school-room was damp and cold. The schoolmaster kept asking the tired, cold children the same questions over and over.

"Who was the first man?"

"Adam," replied a dozen small, weary voices for the tenth time.

"Who was the first woman?" went on the stern voice relentlessly.

"Eve," said the exhausted little voices.

"Who was the meekest man?"

"Moses."

"Who was the oldest man?"

"Methuselah."

"When was Noah's flood?"

"The year 2350 B.C."

Soon Bob knew the answers as well as anyone. He could look at the schoolmaster and answer questions while his thoughts were far away.

THE BIRCH ROD

At last it was time for the noon recess! But even this was a disappointment. His mother's gingerbread which usually tasted so good had no taste at all. He could hardly swallow it for the curious lump that was already in his throat.

After mealtime the older boys made popguns and whistles out of chestnut branches. But Bob could only look on, for he had left his jackknife in his old breeches.

He was almost glad when the bell rang.

But if the morning had seemed long, the afternoon was endless. The sands in the hourglass on Master Johnson's desk seemed to be stuck. The schoolmaster was explaining the meaning of certain mottoes. While Bob wiggled on the hard bench, the schoolmaster discussed the meaning of one motto for a whole hour.

"A man of words and not of deeds
Is like a garden full of weeds."

Bob looked down at his desk. His beautiful copybook lay unopened. His ink had not been touched. And just when Bob thought he was never going to use them, the schoolmaster's voice boomed:

"Open thy copybooks and write the motto I have given thee."

With eager fingers Bob dipped his pen into the ink. The words "garden" and "weeds" somehow made him think of Hans Holzer's land.

So he drew a gently rising hill with his pen. Next he drew a picture of Hans Holzer digging. He forgot about writing the motto. He forgot about Master Caleb Johnson.

Suddenly he was brought up with a start.

"Robert Fulton!" the schoolmaster was shouting. "Thee will stand."

Bob stood up quickly.

"Bring thy copybook to me. Come! Come!"

The class sat up, eyes wide open.

An awful stillness came over the room.

With his knees trembling, Bob walked to the desk in the center of the room. He handed his copybook to the schoolmaster.

Master Johnson studied Mrs. Fulton's writing on the cover.

"The ink is feeble," he said harshly.

Bob's face went red.

"The skating figures on the cover are shameful." The master's eyebrows met in a deep frown. "It is against my conscience that children skate while their elders labor."

Now he turned to the class. "Write in thy copybooks:

"Eat not the bread of idleness."

A dozen pens began scratching while the schoolmaster opened Bob's copybook. There on the very first page he spied the picture of Hans Holzer with his pickax. It was plain that Master Johnson was angered.

"Put forth thy hand!" he commanded as he reached for a birch rod.

Whack! went the rod across Bob's hand.

Whirr! Whack! Whirr! went the rod again. It stung fearfully.

"There!" said the schoolmaster. "That will make thee do something."

"Sir," replied Bob, "I came to have something beaten into my brains and not into my knuckles!"

The schoolmaster's eyes seemed to bulge right out of his head. He could think of nothing to say. He put down his rod. He took off his spectacles.

Just then the late afternoon sun slipped behind a cloud. The room darkened.

"It grows too dark for work," said Master Johnson. "Go home, everyone. Go home."

The Picture

BOB GLANCED up from the Indian broom he was making. How comfortable the kitchen looked! How bright and cheerful after his first horrible day at school!

The evening meal was over. The table board, scrubbed white, stood against the wall. The wooden bowls were lined up on the chimney shelf in a tidy row. And each member of the family was busy with some handiwork.

"Tasks aside!" called Mrs. Fulton. "Story time is come!"

Quickly the children drew their stools in a half circle about the fire.

Even Matilda moved up closer as if to say, "This, now, is the way I like it best: all the children at home, and a warm fire to snooze by."

"Reynard the Fox! Reynard the Fox!" shouted Abraham as he tugged at Mrs. Fulton's apron. "Please, Mamma, tell us the story of the smart fox."

"Pooh!" said Polly, wrinkling her nose. "Abraham would want that every night."

"More than anything I would like a true story," said Bob. "And make it full of Indians, and please to put a boy in it—a boy about my age who meets the Indians."

"A true story! A true one!" cried the girls. "Please, Mamma."

"Mercy me!" laughed Mrs. Fulton. "A true story with Indians, and a lad just turning eight. I'll have to put on my thinking cap."

Abraham's lip began to quiver. He still wanted to hear about the fox.

"Abraham," said Mrs. Fulton, "you may pop the corn tonight. Put just a handful on the long shovel. Peggy will butter and salt it. Now then, let me think . . . ."

For a minute Mrs. Fulton sat thinking. Then her eyes fell on the miniature painting of herself and Mr. Fulton on the chimney shelf.

"I have the *very* story!" she said eagerly.

Outside, the wind howled and scraped the branches of a hemlock tree across the shutters.

"Put a pine log on the hearth, Bob. The sound of its crackling will dull the wind."

With an excited feeling, the children watched Bob lift a great log on the fire. Abraham was impatient. He had the corn on the shovel all ready to pop.

Mrs. Fulton smoothed her apron.

"A little Quaker boy painted the picture on the shelf," she began. "And your father and I never dreamed that he would soon be famous."

"What was his name?" asked Peggy.

"His name was Benjamin West, and a handsome lad he was. Fair, and slender as a birch rod, and quiet and gentle."

At the mention of birch rod, Bob squirmed. To hide his feelings, he poked the fire, although it was already crackling merrily.

"When are the Indians coming?" asked Abraham as he watched the corn jump and swell.

"Hush!" said Belle. "You'll hear about them if you don't fall asleep. Won't he, Mamma?"

"Now, Mother!" exclaimed Bob, his eyes shiny. "Tell us about the boy."

Mrs. Fulton looked from one upturned face to the other. "Once there was a Quaker lad," she began again. "He lived with his mother and his father and five sisters and four brothers in our province of Pennsylvania. He was a poor boy, but he saw things with a clear eye."

"What things?" asked Polly.

"Oh, birds and flowers and cows and trees and houses and people. And he saw them so clear that he was not content just to look at them. He wanted to share the things he saw. So he drew pictures of them."

"But where did he get the materials?" Bob wanted to know.

"He was good at inventing. He made his own ink, and he used poplar boards instead of paper."

"When are the Indians coming?" insisted Abraham.

"One day," said Mrs. Fulton, "Benjamin was alone in the woods. He was drawing the picture of a robin. Suddenly three Indians stole up behind him. Their footsteps made no sound.

"Neither Benjamin nor the robin heard them. Benjamin went right on dipping into the pot of black ink and sketching away with his goose-quill pen. And the robin went right on combing his feathers with his beak.

"For a long time the Indians watched over Benjamin's shoulder. Then, without any warning, one of them snapped a twig."

Pop! went the pine log just then, and a live ember split almost in Matilda's face.

The children rocked in laughter as Matilda sprang out for the safe harbor of Mrs. Fulton's skirts and hid her head.

"Go on, Mamma!" urged Polly. "What happened after Benjamin saw the Indians?"

"At the sound of the twig," whispered Mrs. Fulton, "Benjamin jumped just like Matilda. Then he turned around and saw three tall Indians right behind him. They carried spears and they wore headdresses of eagle feathers."

"'Oh!' said Benjamin with a start. 'Oh, oh!'"

"The Indians made no answer. Instead they pointed to the robin which had flown to a treetop. Then they pointed to their chests which were bright with red and yellow paint.

"Afraid as he was, Benjamin could see that the Indians were asking him a question. They wanted to know why he had not painted the robin's breast red."

"How could he?" exclaimed Belle. "He had no paints."

Mrs. Fulton nodded and went on. "Suddenly the Indians started off in the direction of the creek. They motioned the boy to follow.

"By now Benjamin could see that these were friendly Indians. Besides, he was curious. So he picked up his poplar board and followed along.

"Soon they reached a sandy ledge. Here the leader stopped. He scooped some red earth out of the bank. Then he picked up a smooth stone and ground the clay in a most workmanlike manner. Meanwhile the second Indian had gone down to the creek and filled a gourd with water."

"And did they mix the water and the red earth?" asked Bob in excitement.

"They did indeed.

"They mixed it until the water turned a rich brownish red. And what is more, they made yellow paint from yellow earth."

The children were so interested they nearly swallowed their popcorn whole.

"Then the Indian leader put his hand on Benjamin's head and set him down. He took the poplar board from under Benjamin's arm and put it on his lap. The second Indian held out the gourd filled with the red paint. And the third Indian held out a shell filled with the yellow paint and pointed to the bird.

"Benjamin was a sharp lad and caught on in a twinkling. First he dipped his finger in the red paint and colored the robin's breast. Then he dipped his finger in the yellow paint and gave the robin a bright yellow beak."

"Ho, ho!" exclaimed Abraham. "This is better than Reynard the Fox. What happened then, Mamma?"

"The Indians grunted in satisfaction and turned to go back into the forest."

"'Wait!' cried Benjamin. 'Wait! Wait!'

"He had a present for them, and it was his most prized possession."

"Not his jackknife!" cried Bob.

"Yes, his jackknife.

"Then feeling very happy, he flew for home. He wanted to show the picture to his mother and his father and his five sisters and his four brothers."

"What did they say?" asked Peggy.

"Well, Mr. West was a Quaker, and you know Quakers do not approve of bright colors. When he saw them he scowled. Then he paced the floor.

"But Mrs. West threw her arms around Benjamin and declared it the most beautiful picture she had ever seen. And besides, she told Benjamin he could have some of her bluing which she kept in a little dye pot in the kitchen. So before Benjamin was eight years old, he could make every color of the rainbow from red clay and yellow clay, and his mother's bluing."

Bob Fulton hugged himself in delight. He liked true stories, especially when they were full of Indians and war paint. He picked up the bellows and blew on the fire because he felt good toward the whole wide world.

FIVE LITTLE FULTONS GO TO BED

"Now, Polly," said Mrs. Fulton, "you may pass the apples, and Abraham, you may pass the horehound candy. One apiece for everybody."

"But what happened to Benjamin West when he grew up?" Bob wanted to know.

"Why, he won fame and fortune. He went to London to paint for the king! And he's there this very minute."

The little kitchen grew noisy with talk and laughter and the crunching of apples.

"Hush!" called Mrs. Fulton. "The clock in the tower strikes eight."

At the last bonging note, Abraham kneeled at his mother's feet. The older children rested their heads on their arms and each one knelt before his own three-legged stool.

The heat from the hearth warmed their backs. And inside, they were warmed with happiness.

Now five soft voices whispered into the quiet:

"Be near me, Lord Jesus, I ask Thee to stay
Close by me forever, and love me, I pray.
Bless all the dear children in Thy tender care,
And take us to Heaven to live with Thee there."

At the very end, Bob said a silent prayer of his own: "Please, God, let me draw like Benjamin West."

Then Peggy lighted a candle, and the five little Fultons climbed up the ladder to the loft.

Bob sank into his feather bed and fell asleep almost at once. He did not even dream that one day Benjamin West would be his teacher.

Discovery at Conestoga Creek

BOB THREW the lump of charcoal into the forge. He looked at his drawing in disgust. The charcoal made wide, fuzzy lines. He wanted to draw fine lines on his plan.

The gunsmith slipped up behind Bob. "Suffering pumpkins," he cried, "you've made a picture of a gun!"

"But, sir, the trigger," said Bob, shaking his head. "I wanted to put a better guard on it. And I wanted to draw a wild duck on the stock. But the charcoal won't make fine lines."

Gunsmith stroked his chin thoughtfully. Then his face lighted as he had an idea.

"You've been to school near six months now. Any boy with all that schooling could use pen and ink for fine lines."

Bob hung his head. "I didn't mean to tell you, sir, but . . ."

"What is it, son?"

"Your two pennies were wasted. My ink is spoiled. It was the grease from the candles spoiled it."

The gunsmith took a live coal out of the fire with his tongs. He lighted his clay pipe. Then he waited for Bob to explain.

"There have been meetings at the schoolhouse at night," Bob said. "Our inkstands had to serve as candlesticks. And the next day when we used them for ink, our writing appeared greasy, and we couldn't use the ink."

"Fie!" the gunsmith puffed and snorted. "Grown folk have no business meeting in school. If I had my way now, I'd . . . "

But he never finished what he had to say. Just then his eyes caught the little tobacco shop down the road. Mr. Demuth, the owner, had thrown open the shutters. Now he was placing the tiny carved figure of a gentleman on the shelf outside the window. Mr. Demuth was always ready for business at half past seven sharp.

"Quick, lad! Off to school or the birch rods will warm your hide!"

A CURIOUS BLACK ROCK

It was a fine May morning. Bob never liked to reach school too early. Whenever he did, Master Johnson made him cut and mend all the goose-quill pens! So he took the roundabout way along Conestoga Creek.

He poked along the shore with a sharp stick. Nearly always he found something exciting here. One day it had been a huge crayfish hiding beneath a stone. When he touched it, the crayfish swam rapidly away—backward! Another day he came upon a sunfish scooping out a nest in the sand. It was using its nose and fins for a shovel!

Suddenly Bob stopped still. What was this? He tapped his stick along a thin strip of black in the river bank. What could it be? It looked like charcoal! No, it was grayer than charcoal. He took out his jackknife and chipped off a piece. He tried it on a rock. It left a black mark!

With eager fingers he filled his pocket handkerchief with more chips.

Then he ran back to show the gunsmith.

"I've found a strange kind of rock," he cried. "Try it, sir! It writes!"

Mr. Messersmith cleaned his hand on his breeches. Then he took one of the chips and made an x on the back of his hand.

"So it does!" he exclaimed. And his smile grew so wide that it showed the dark hole where his teeth were missing.

"I aim to make something of it, sir. John Cope, my schoolmate, says his father owns a pencil. He says it is made of something called black lead. And the lead fits into a wooden jacket. I believe this is black lead, sir!"

School was forgotten. Bob never gave it another thought. And if the gunsmith remembered, he said nothing. Instead, he whistled a lively tune as he went back to his work.

Bob had no time to build footstools out of bricks this morning. He just jumped for the things he could not reach.

"Whoops!" He was up in the air. He was reaching for the mortar and pestle on a high shelf. He could just touch it.

Mr. Messersmith clapped his hands over his eyes. He hoped the mortar would not crash to the floor. It did not.

With a sigh of relief, he went back to making an iron rim for a wagon wheel.

Bob put the black chips in the mortar. Then he began pounding and grinding them. He could not help laughing to himself. Why, he could pound and pound without getting the least bit tired! How different this was from stirring hasty pudding! This was fun.

Next he sifted the powder. Once. Twice. Three times. Finally it was fine enough to suit him. He was ready for the next process.

"Sir," said Bob, "I need to borrow a lump of your sulphur. The man at the chemist shop says hot sulphur makes things stick together."

Gunsmith nodded.

And presently a ladle holding lead and sulphur was heating in the fire.

First Bob hopped around to the back of the forge to pump the bellows. Then he hopped back to look at the melting lead. Then he stirred it. Then back to pump the bellows.

At last he set the mixture aside to cool.

"I declare!" chuckled the gunsmith. "You 'mind me of a grasshopper with your jumping."

"Now I am ready to make the wood jacket!" exclaimed Bob.

He bounded up the ladder and took one of the pine shingles stored among the rafters. With his jackknife he cut two small strips off the shingle. They were no longer than a ruler and no wider than his thumb.

He took a quick little sniff of the freshly-cut wood. What a nice piny smell!

Next he heated a slender bar of iron in the forge. As soon as it was red-hot, he burned a groove in each strip of wood.

"I aim to make the lead fit in this little groove, sir," said Bob proudly.

Mr. Messersmith raised his eyebrows. "It will be magic if you do. Your mixture looks like Saturday's baking to me!"

Bob hummed as he kneaded the doughy mixture. He was glad his mother could not see him. She might put him to baking bread!

The gunsmith had only half an eye on his wheel. With a smile of pleasure he watched Bob.

Tap! Tap! sounded the mallet. And tap, tap, tap, tap, went Bob's heart. The lead was shaping up. It was growing longer and longer. It was growing rounder and rounder.

"Now the lead is ready," cried Bob.

Carefully he spread a thin layer of glue along the strips of wood.

Then he fitted the two pieces of wood around the lead. He pressed them firmly together. And all the while he pranced around the shop as wild as a colt.

At last he owned a pencil! He took out his jackknife and whittled a sharp point.

Then, suddenly, he thought about school.

TARDY AGAIN

The door of the little Quaker school was closed. There was not a child in sight. Not even a rabbit! With his hand on the latch, Bob stood a minute, remembering. Just six months ago he had stood like this. Only then he did not own a pencil. He would be the only boy in school who had a pencil now. Even the schoolmaster did not have one.

He wondered what to do. Should he go in? Or should he turn around and go home? Should he face the stern schoolmaster? Or the hurt look in his mother's eye? He decided that he would rather face the schoolmaster.

Suddenly the door opened from within, and Robert Fulton fell almost on top of the school-master! He jumped backwards.

For an instant it looked as if Master Johnson was going to explode. His face was fiery red. His eyes bulged fearfully.

Bob stammered. He stood first on one foot, and then on the other.

"Do not wiggle and twist!" barked the school-master. "Stand still!"

The children on their benches leaned around in excitement. The girls were frightened. A few began to sniffle into their pocket handkerchiefs. No one had ever been this late before. There was no telling what the punishment would be!

Schoolmaster Johnson marched back to his desk. He took hold of his birch rods. "Tell the children," he snapped, "why thee is late."

"I have pounded out a pencil," said Bob. And he could not help smiling as he added, "It makes a fine line. Please try it, sir."

The schoolmaster looked at the pencil in awe. He dropped his birch rods. He pushed his wig to one side and scratched his head. In all his lifetime he had seen only three pencils. This was as neat as any.

The class sat up in surprise. Everyone wondered what was going to happen.

Now the schoolmaster was putting on his spectacles. He was trying to find the seam where the two pieces of wood were glued. Next, he wrote with the pencil on a piece of birch bark.

"Well, I'll declare!" he breathed. "I will not deny that it works. I declare, thee can make much out of little, Robert Fulton!"

And then Schoolmaster Caleb Johnson did something that no one had ever seen him do before. He leaned over and patted Bob on the back.

Bob's head was in a whirl. Why, the schoolmaster is nice, he said to himself. Exceedingly nice! He let out a great sigh of happiness.

"The sun is overhead," spoke the master in a quieter voice than usual. "It is time for the noontide meal."

Out in the schoolyard the boys flocked around Bob. They could hardly eat their lunches for excitement. Questions flew. Everyone wanted to know just how to make a pencil.

But this noontide Bob was hungry. He bit off a great piece of gingerbread. How good it tasted! He thought his mother had never before made such good gingerbread.

Between bites he answered all the questions, the wise ones and the foolish ones. In the back of his mind, however, he was at the gunsmith shop. He was thinking of the half-finished drawing of the gun. At last he could draw fine lines!

Major André

"YOU SCARED of the redcoats?" John Cope asked Bob one afternoon.

John was Bob's schoolmate. He was three years older than Bob. He liked to feel that he was bigger and braver than Bob. He had a way of asking questions suddenly. Sometimes the questions felt sharp, like a bee sting.

The two boys were walking along the river on their way home from school. It was autumn in the year 1775. For over six months the American colonies had been fighting for their independence. The boys heard a great deal about the battles that had been fought.

Already there were hundreds of British prisoners in Lancaster. They were called "redcoats" because of their bright red uniforms.

The very word "redcoat" sent many children screaming for home.

"Well?" demanded John Cope. "Are you or aren't you scared of the redcoats?"

Bob did not know how to answer. Some redcoats were mean and ugly fellows. He was afraid of them. Some were good-natured. And these he was not afraid of.

Just then Abraham came running to meet them. How glad Bob was to see him! It gave him time to think.

Abraham took a deep breath. "Could we play whoop and hide? Could we play leapfrog? Could we play hopscotch?" he asked.

John was losing his temper. "That brother of yours!" he burst out. "Must he always tag along? He can ask more questions than . . ."

"Than you!" laughed Bob.

"Humph!" said John. "I was going to invite you to my house. We have been asked to board a redcoat. He was captured by General Montgomery in Canada. His name is Major André, and he owns a box of paints."

"A box of paints!" repeated Bob.

"Not only that, he has five paintbrushes."

"Not camel's-hair brushes!"

"Yes. Camel's-hair brushes." John nodded in glee. Then he picked up a flat stone and skimmed it across the river to show his skill.

"Oh, look!" exclaimed Abraham. "It skipped three times! Can you always skip three times?"

"No!" snapped John. "I don't very often skip just three times. Most always I can skip five times. Now let us talk."

Then he turned to Bob. "The Major is teaching me how to paint," he boasted. "Now are you scared of redcoats?"

Bob grabbed Abraham's hand and dashed toward home. "I'll be over right after chores tonight," he called back.

John Cope rocked back on his heels and laughed. He liked Bob Fulton. "Even if he is only nine," John said aloud, "he is brave and he is smart."

AIM WELL!

The moon was full. It threw a magic white light over Lancaster.

Bob was hurrying to the Copes' house. As he turned in at the gate of the Quaker family, he ran into Mr. and Mrs. Cope.

"Bless thee!" laughed Mr. Cope. "Thee is in great haste."

"John is expecting thee, Robert," said Mrs. Cope. "We are on our way to the meetinghouse. Thee can let thyself in."

Bob thanked Mr. and Mrs. Cope. Then he lifted the latch and entered their comfortable stone house.

On the braided rug, before a leaping fire, were John and his young brothers, Bill and Thomas. They were playing marbles. And kneeling right with the boys was Major André.

The Major was splendid in his scarlet coat and white breeches. The firelight danced on his gold buttons and on the silver spurs on his heels. It made Bob blink.

"He must be man-grown," thought Bob, "and quite old to be a major. Probably in his twenties, though he looks to be not much older than John. How fine he looks!"

John and Bill and Thomas did not even hear Bob come in. They were lost in their game.

Only Major André turned around. He gave Bob a quick smile. It seemed to say, "We can be friends at once."

John was having his turn. He was winning. He had most of the marbles in a little bag behind him.

Click! He knocked the last marble out of the ring. Then he laughed so heartily that Bob laughed, too.

"Oh, it's you!" he said. He jumped up and drew Bob into the circle.

"Major André, this is my friend Bob Fulton."

The Major stood up and shook hands with Bob. "I understand," he said, "that you have a turn for art. It would please me to have you join our little class."

"Oh, sir," said Bob quickly, "it would please me, too! It would please me very much!"

"One more game of marbles," begged Thomas. "John took all my best ones. Just one more game. Please, Major."

Bob's face fell. He had come to see a box of paints, not to play marbles.

"One more game it is," laughed the Major. "Come join us, Bob. The dark blue center of the rug is the ring."

"I haven't any marbles, sir. But I have three hickory nuts in my pocket. They make fine shooters."

Now Bob was in the game. He placed his two hickory nuts in the ring.

The three Cope boys and the Major each put in two shiny marbles.

"Bob Fulton shall be first," said the Major. "Knuckle down, and aim well!"

Bob kneeled down. He rested his knuckle on the rug. He bent his head to one side. He squinted one eye. He thought he could knock two marbles out of the ring with one try.

Pfft came the little noise made by his thumb.

The hickory nut shot into the ring. Clickety-click, it knocked one marble against the other. Then both went bounding across the rug.

"I wish I owned a hickory nut," pouted Thomas. "I'm sure I could shoot better if I had a hickory nut."

"Pooh!" sniffed John. "You'd forget and eat it in the middle of a game."

Bob pocketed the two marbles.

He shot again and took two more.

The third time he missed. Then everyone sang to him:

> "Knuckle down to your taw,
> Aim well, shoot away,
> Keep out of the ring —
> You'll soon learn to play!"

Bill, Thomas, and John each had his turn. Bill knocked one marble out of the ring, and John three. All of them were quiet as they watched these shots.

Now only the two hickory nuts were left.

"I'd like to try your home-grown shooter," the Major said to Bob.

He took great care not to sit back on his spurs. He took great care to line up his play. Then, to everyone's merriment, the nut flew across the room and landed in the fire.

Quick as a flash Bob rescued it. He wanted to get the game over. "I've got to knock my hickory nuts out of the ring," he said to himself. "It's getting late."

He scrunched down. He rested his knuckle on the rug. He took aim.

Pfft! came the little noise made by his thumb.

A cry of relief broke from Bob. The shooter had knocked one nut against the other and sent them both flying.

"Bravo!" shouted Major André. "Bravo! Bravo! That shot took real skill, Bob. You are an expert player."

Before anyone could suggest another game, Bob stood up. He just couldn't waste any more time away from the art lesson.

"Let's not play for keeps," he said. And he began returning the marbles. Two to the Major, and two apiece to John and Bill and little Thomas. The hickory nuts, too, he gave to Thomas.

"Now, sir," cried Bob as he faced the Major, "now, sir, if you please—I came to see your paintbox!"

The Box
of Paints

THE CLOCK in the meetinghouse tower struck
seven, then eight, then nine. Bob did not even
hear it.

Bill and little Thomas had fallen asleep on the
settle. The fire was low. The room had grown
cold. The candle on the table was sputtering.

But Major André and his two pupils, John and
Bob, were neither tired nor cold.

The Major was actually letting the boys use his
paintbox. It was more exciting than anything they
had ever seen. They had never realized the pos-
sibilities for depicting such delicate shades of
color before.

Along one side of the box there were tiny bottles. These were filled with oils. Along the other side were tiny boxes. These were filled with earth colors. Down the center of the box was a row of tiny bowls for mixing the colors. Fastened to the lid were a whole parade of camel's-hair brushes. There were slender ones, fat ones, and medium ones. They felt almost as soft as the fluff in a milkweed pod.

Now the Major was saying, "Bob, your work could be smoother and softer. Lay the shades on more gradually. Wash them over again and again, but never until the paper is quite dry."

Just then the latch lifted, and Mr. and Mrs. Cope came in. They were amazed to find that Bill and little Thomas were not in bed.

Then everyone began talking at once.

I beg you to forgive my not sending Bill and little Thomas to their room," the Major said to Mrs. Cope.

"Oh, Mother, it is not Major André's fault," spoke up John. "I asked questions in a loud voice whenever the clock struck."

Bob reached for his three-cornered hat. He did not try to hide his happiness. "It is all my fault," he said. "We've been learning to put things on paper. May I come again?"

Mr. and Mrs. Cope laughed. There was nothing of the stern Quaker about them. "Come often, Robert," they said. "As often as the Major can put up with thee and John."

"NICE MATILDA!"

Bob finished milking Bessie, the cow. Bessie lived in half of the barn, and Bob had his workroom in the other half.

Bob's only furniture was a little shelf which held his jugs of homemade colors. These were neatly labeled in his own handwriting:

RED	YELLOW	BLUE
from	from	from the bark of
berry juice	the earth	the blue ash tree

BROWN	INK
from	from the bark of
walnut hull	the goosefoot maple

Now Bob sat upon the milking stool in front of the barn door. He was trying to draw a picture of Hans Holzer's fields. The canal and the machinery looked very well in pen strokes. But the sky looked all wrong.

How could he practice what the Major taught when he had no brush! He set the poplar board down and sighed with discouragement.

Just then Matilda sprang on Bob's lap and climbed up on his shoulder. Her long tail swept across his face.

"Why, how very soft it feels!" said Bob.

He stroked Matilda's fur with a new light in his eye. "Nice Matilda!" he whispered.

Matilda blinked at Bob with a wise little look. The end of her tail twitched. "Don't you be getting ideas," she seemed to say.

"You wouldn't miss a few hairs, would you?" he whispered into her silky ear. "You see, Matilda, I need a soft brush. Come to think of it, I believe Benjamin West made a brush from the fur of his cat."

Matilda looked at him suspiciously and walked away. She settled herself to sleep on the other side of the fireplace.

"Oh, I stand willing to pay for the brush." Bob laughed. "I will give you the top of Bessie's rich yellow cream. And I will give you my helpings of fish. Maybe even a chicken liver now and again, and anything else I know you like."

In a fever of excitement Bob went to work.

He noticed that the tip of Matilda's tail formed a natural paintbrush. So he cut the hair with great care.

He wanted them to form the same little point for his brush. He wanted to copy Matilda's tail as nearly as he could.

"There, Matilda! That didn't hurt, did it?" asked Bob.

For answer, Matilda streaked toward the kitchen door.

Now Bob plucked a long hair from his own head. He wound it around the tiny bundle of cat hairs as tight as he could wind. Then he glued the bundle into his goose-quill.

"Heigh-ho!" he shouted. "Who needs a camel to make brushes?"

He dipped his new brush into the jug of blue paint and painted a cloudless blue sky over Hans Holzer's land.

All during supper Matilda rubbed against Bob's leg as if to remind him of their secret pact. Bob kept his word. His hand carried food below the table board as often as above.

In less than a week Bob needed more brushes—slender ones, fat ones, medium-sized ones.

Matilda grew to be a most peculiar-looking cat. She became plump as a pumpkin. But, oh, her fur! It was as patchy as a rag bag.

Soon Matilda was not alone in her strange appearance. All over Lancaster boys and girls began making paintbrushes. And the cats of Lancaster were the most curious cats in all the thirteen colonies.

A STRANGE FISHING TRIP

The Major's lessons were growing fewer. Soon they would have to stop altogether. Even before the war, paper had been scarce. Now it was almost impossible to get. The Major disapproved of using birch bark or poplar boards in place of paper. He did not like to see the fine trees destroyed.

"Someday," he told the boys, "your country will have need of its trees. You may use my pieces of canvas as long as they last."

Before long all the canvases had been used, and there were no more lessons.

Mrs. Fulton knew that Bob missed his lessons. She tried to help him forget by sending him off on adventures.

"Mercy on us!" she said to Bob one afternoon. "My cupboard is as bare as old Mother Hubbard's. How good some stewed mussels would taste! Why don't you and John Cope gather mussels this afternoon? Abraham and the girls will milk Bessie and do your chores."

Bob's face lighted. He was off in a flash, swinging two wooden buckets.

"Oh, Bob," Mrs. Fulton called after him, "you may ask John to supper."

John was anxious to go along. He hoped they would find a pearl in one of the mussel shells.

Soon the boys were wading along the shores of Conestoga Creek. The water felt icy cold, but it was clear as crystal. The grooves left by the mussels were easy to see.

In no time at all the boys had their buckets filled. Then they dropped down on the bank and let the sun and the wind dry their legs.

"Let's open a few shells and hunt for pearls," suggested John. "I'll find a stick to pry them open. Probably we can find a whole bag of pearls if we try."

"Sh!" whispered Bob. He dropped a handful of mussels on the shore and hid behind a willow tree. He motioned for John to follow. John was puzzled. He didn't see any reason to hide.

"See that oyster catcher bird wading along the edge of the river?" he whispered.

"What kind of bird?" asked John.

"That oyster catcher! It's a rare bird. Wait and see what it does to those mussels."

The boys waited. John was beginning to think the whole idea rather tiresome. The bird continued to run along the shore on its long pink legs. John couldn't see that the bird was going anywhere or doing anything interesting.

Then suddenly it rose into the air and circled right over the mussels lying on the shore. At last it swooped low and thrust its sharp-edged beak between the double shells of the mussel. Quickly it ate the live mussel inside.

Then away it soared until it was only a speck in the sky.

Bob and John hurried over to the opened mussel. They admired the pearly blue-white layer.

"Mussel shells would be fine for mixing paints!" exclaimed John.

Suddenly a cry broke from Bob. "John! John! We could paint on them. Let's try it tonight. I'm sure it'll work, and the Major can't disapprove of using shells!"

The boys grabbed up their buckets and raced for home. They helped Mrs. Fulton wash the mussels. They helped her put them into the stewpan. And when the shells opened, they picked out the meat for her. They could hardly wait for supper to be over.

Much to Peggy's and Belle's amazement, the boys even scrubbed the table board!

At last they were mixing their paints. "I have plenty of colors for both of us," said Bob.

"Where is your oil for mixing the colors?" asked John.

"Skimmed milk is just as good," replied Bob. "Especially if you don't have oil!"

The boys worked on their pictures while Polly and Abraham watched. Bob's picture took form quickly. He was creating a picture of something that had always interested him.

"Why, that's Deter Gumpf's boat!" cried Polly. "I'm going to show him the picture."

John's picture was not very clear. He had to tell the children that it was an oyster catcher bird. When the pictures were finished, John and Bob took their mussel shells to show Major André. In great excitement they burst into his room.

The Major was busy writing a letter, but he laid his pen aside. He studied the pictures close up. Then he walked away from them, still looking as he walked. "They show promise," he said. Then he added thoughtfully, "I shall soon be going away. I should be happier to know that my box of paints was in good hands. I give it to you boys."

There was a long silence. The boys looked at each other. They did not know what to say.

John was first to get his breath. "Bob's picture is good," he said. "Bob can make you see what he sees. I think I would like to give the paintbox to him. The whole box."

And he placed it in Bob's hands.

Bob Serves His Country

THE WAR went on. By 1778 it reached out and touched all of the thirteen colonies.

The city of Lancaster seemed to change overnight. Men came flocking in from the fields. They brought their old rusty firearms with them. They were in a hurry to have them repaired. They wanted to join the army.

There was a great need for new guns, too. Mr. Messersmith and all the other gunsmiths had more work than they could manage. They hired more men and tried to teach them the work. Then they had to stretch ropes around their shops to keep out curious people.

Armed guards stood at the doors. Signs were posted. They read:

NO VISITORS ALLOWED

These signs were not intended for young Bob Fulton, however. All the gunsmiths welcomed Bob. Even though he was only twelve, his head was full of ideas. And his ideas worked. When he suggested a change in the design of a gun, the men listened with respect.

What amazed the gunsmiths was this. Bob would take an old gun over to the workbench. Then he would pull out one of his handmade pencils and sketch the gun. He would take note of three things—the size of the bore, the weight of the ball, and a given charge of powder of a certain test. Then he figured out on paper about how far the gun would shoot. When the men tested the guns, Bob's figures were accurate.

The older gunsmiths shook their heads in wonder. "I declare!" they said. "It isn't lead that's in your pencil. It's magic!"

Never was Bob so busy. Nor so happy. He did not even mind when the new apprentice boys spoke of him as "that Quicksilver Bob."

They had seen him buy mercury, or quicksilver as it was called, at the chemist shop. And they were provoked when Bob did not explain his experiments with quicksilver.

Soon the gunsmiths had picked up the nickname, too, but it sounded pleasant when *they* said it.

"There's a nickname that fits," Mr. Messersmith told one of the new workmen. "Bob here is quick to move, like quicksilver itself!"

From sunup to sundown the shops were open. Bob worked before school in the morning, and every night after school. Even on Sundays he worked all day.

Before the war, the people of Lancaster had not even cooked on Sunday. Now everyone looked on Sunday as a busy day — an extra day to help win the fight for freedom.

General George Washington was calling for more guns to drive the British out of New York. Young Lieutenant George Rogers Clark was calling for more arms to drive the British out of the Ohio and Mississippi Valleys. The gunsmiths could not keep up with the orders.

With every campaign, government orders for guns and gunpowder mounted. And every day farmers and woodsmen brought in more arms — flintlock guns, matchlock guns, old squirrel guns, even pistols.

And still there were not enough firearms for all the men who wanted to fight.

Bob felt as important as any soldier. He helped repair old rifles and design new ones. He helped make bullet molds. He cast bullets.

When lead grew scarce, he went from house to house, collecting pewter. He was so eager in his pleas that housewives often gave him their tea sets, their candlesticks, their pitchers.

Each woman said, "This will make more bullets. It will help to bring Amos (or Peter or Samuel) home to me sooner."

THE NEW APPRENTICE

Early one Sunday morning, Bob reported at Mr. Messersmith's as usual. A new apprentice boy met him at the door and handed him an old-fashioned musket. This boy was older than the other apprentices, and quieter. Bob had never seen him before.

"I changed the hammer according to your design," he said. "Now Mr. Messersmith wants you to test it. You might be eating roast partridge for your supper."

Bob wondered why the boy's hands shook when he turned over the gun.

"Maybe because he's new and strange," thought Bob, as he slung a powder horn over his shoulder and set out for the hills.

It was a bright March day. Bob took a deep breath. The air smelled new, clean, and warm.

He strode along, whistling "Yankee Doodle" at the top of his lungs. Suddenly he stopped in the middle of a note. He spied a fat squirrel leaping wildly from one tree to another. It would take skill to hit him.

Bob raised the gun to take aim when suddenly he noticed that something looked wrong with the back of the gun barrel. A piece of round wood stuck out of it.

The squirrel was forgotten. Bob loosened the piece of wood. He stared at the gun. He could hardly believe what he saw. He turned the gun over and examined it closely.

"What is *this*?" he breathed. "A hole has been drilled clean through the barrel to the gunpowder chamber. It has been plugged with this piece of wood."

His knees suddenly went limp. He knew that if he had fired the musket, the plug would have been driven into his face.

He laughed shakily. "I guess I drove the wood out a little way when I rammed the powder and ball down the muzzle," he said thoughtfully.

He pocketed the wooden plug. Then, as fast as he could travel with the heavy musket, he ran for the nearest gun factory.

William Henry's shop on Mill Creek was less than a mile away.

"Morning, Quicksilver Bob," the workmen greeted him.

No one questioned him. They were used to having him come in, work for an hour or so, and go on.

Bob worked carefully. He fitted and riveted a steel plug into the hole in the barrel.

By noon the gun barrel was as good as new. Now he could shoot in safety.

With a serious look, he set out again for the hills. Then he began hunting with a fierce determination.

ROAST PARTRIDGE FOR SUPPER

Bob glanced at the sun. It looked as if the horizon had cut it neatly in half. He looked at his bag. A smile of satisfaction spread over his face as he hurried back to Mr. Messersmith's shop. Both apprentices, as well as the blacksmith, were still working.

The new apprentice was making notes in a small book. When he saw Bob, he dropped the book. His face went green. It was as if he had seen a ghost.

Supper was late that night. But it was worth waiting for.

"Mother, this partridge tastes especially good," said Bob.

Mrs. Fulton was proud to have Bob mention her cooking. She had no idea how closely her boy had escaped injury. Nor did she know that only this afternoon he had caught a spy.

Fireworks

BOB CALLED UP to the loft where the children were hanging herbs to dry. "Peggy! Belle! Polly! Abraham! Come down and see!"

The children scrambled down the stairs, almost upsetting one another in their eagerness. "What is it? What is it? they cried.

Bob pointed to the half-burned candles in the candle chest. "Look at them—nineteen in all!" he exclaimed. "And Fourth of July only three days away!"

Polly danced around the table board. "Why, we'll have candles to burn in every window!" she laughed.

"And some for outdoors," added Belle.

Abraham sighed. "Of all holidays," he said, "I like the Fourth of July best."

"Why do you?" asked Bob.

"Because it is good and noisy. Bells ring. Guns pop. Drums and trumpets to march by. And at night the candles."

"Candles don't make noise," said Polly.

"Yes, they do!" insisted Abraham. "They sputter. Besides, they make a noisy light."

Everyone laughed. Abraham had his own way of arguing.

"This year July Fourth will be more exciting than ever," Bob promised.

"Why?" asked Abraham.

"Because it is the birthday of our country," answered Polly.

"How old is our country?" asked Abraham.

"Our country will be exactly two years old, and we are winning the war!" Bob explained.

112

"I think it would be fit," said Peggy in her most grown-up manner, "if you divided the candles. Then we could place our own candles where they would be best seen."

"Oh, yes!" shouted the others. "Divide up! Divide up!"

"That's what I plan to do," said Bob.

"Mind you, children, only the candle *ends* are to be used," said Mrs. Fulton. "Tallow is scarce. We cannot afford to burn the four longer candles. Soon," she smiled, "we shall be calling this our treasure chest instead of our candle chest. We may not have any candles to burn except for special occasions."

Dividing the candle ends was no easy matter! Some of them were only a few inches long. Some were bent from the summer heat. Some were cracked. But Bob was so fair that no one grumbled. Each of them began to look for the best places to show the candles.

For a whole year—ever since last July Fourth—the children had been saving candles.

Often they had gone up to bed without a candle. The strings of herbs hanging in the loft were scary-looking by moonlight. Abraham would stay very close to Bob, and Polly hung onto her two big sisters.

"Think of all the candles we shall have by July Fourth!" Bob would say, as everyone crawled into bed in the dark.

Lessons, too, were read by firelight to save precious candles.

And now, all the saving seemed worthwhile, for each of the Fultons had three candle ends!

"I declare!" exclaimed Mrs. Fulton. "I see five pairs of eyes brighter than any candlelight."

Now the children scampered off in five different directions. They were going to hide their candles until the night of July Fourth.

Bob hurried out to the barn with his. Just as he laid them on the shelf, he heard a shrill whistle. He peered around the barn door.

"Oh, halloo there, Chris," he called. "Come on over. I haven't seen you around the shop for the last few days."

Chris was Christopher Gumpf, son of one of the workmen at Mr. Messersmith's.

"Want to show you something," called Chris. "Come along."

"You look mighty gloomy," Bob said, "especially as it is so near the Fourth."

Chris snorted at mention of the Fourth.

Bob almost had to run to keep up with Chris. He was older than Bob, and his legs were long.

"Where you going?" questioned Bob.

Chris did not answer. He only walked faster. At last he pointed ahead to the meetinghouse.

An excited group of men and boys had gathered about the door. Bob slipped into the crowd.

By standing on tiptoe, he could see the sign that was posted on the door. It read:

> "The excessive heat of the weather, the present scarcity of candles . . . induce the Council to recommend to the inhabitants to forbear illuminating the city on Saturday evening next, July 4th
>
> "By order,
> "Timothy Matlack, sec.
> "July 1, 1778"

Bob and Chris were speechless. They walked home, too disappointed to talk. They had been looking forward to Independence Day for a year. Because of the war, they had few holidays.

BOB MAKES A TRADE

That night after all the children were asleep, Bob crept down the dark stairs.

Mrs. Fulton was sitting in the dooryard, enjoying the coolness of the night air.

"Mother," said Bob as he sat down on the step bedside her, "have you told Abraham and the girls that we are forbidden to light our candles?"

"No, son. I hadn't the heart to tell them."

"I'd like to ask you something, Mother."

"Yes?"

"Could I trade our candle ends for gunpowder? With gunpowder I could make skyrockets. They would be brighter than a hundred candles and far more beautiful."

For a long time there was no answer. Only a catbird sang to the moon.

At last Mrs. Fulton spoke. "If you had not worked with gunpowder, I should say no. But I trust you, Bob—far beyond your years. Go ahead with your shooting candles. Make them light the sky. But oh, Bob, do be careful!"

Bob's heart did a somersault. He was sure he had the best mother in all the thirteen colonies. He had hardly expected to get her consent.

At breakfast the next morning Bob told his plan to the excited Fultons.

And presently out from five hiding places came a total of fifteen candle ends.

With the candle chest held tightly under his arm, Bob hurried to visit Mr. Fisher. Mr. Fisher was a brushmaker who made gunpowder when he was not making brushes.

Bob laid the fifteen candle ends on the brushmaker's workbench.

"I should like to exchange these for gunpowder," he said.

Mr. Fisher shook his head in amazement. "You mean to say that you are willing to give up your candles?"

"Yes, sir. The government does not wish us to light our houses with candles. So I aim to light the sky with shooting candles."

"But that seems impossible for a lad to do," said the brushmaker kindly.

"Nothing is impossible, sir," smiled Bob. "You just watch for my rockets in the sky on the Fourth of July."

Then he waited while Mr. Fisher weighed the gunpowder.

"Be careful, lad," Mr. Fisher warned.

Next he went to the variety store owned by Mr. Cossart. There he bought four little packages of dry powder—to make red, yellow, green, and blue lights. He bought also some sheets of pasteboard.

Mr. Cossart started to roll the pasteboard.

"Oh, if it please you, sir! Please do not roll the sheets," said Bob. "I aim to make tubes out of them for my skyrockets."

Mr. Cossart's mouth opened wide. "You can't make skyrockets, son. That's an impossibility," he said. "You'd need special equipment."

"Nothing is impossible, sir," smiled Bob. "Watch the heavens on the Fourth of July."

"Bessie," said Bob to the cow, "until next Saturday I shall be milking you in the meadow. 'Twill be safer for you. Besides, I need the whole barn, and I don't want to frighten you."

All morning Bob worked. He boiled starch. He stirred it into the gunpowder to form a doughy mixture. He separated the mixture into four batches. Then he added one of the dry powders to each batch—to make red, yellow, blue, and green lights. And finally he shaped the rockets and pressed them into pasteboard tubes. He wouldn't let Polly and Abraham help him.

July Fourth came at last. The sun had set. The parades were over. Supper dishes were put away. Chores were done.

Now the people were leaving their houses to stroll and visit on the village green. They gathered in little groups under the trees. They talked of the war, the parades, and the weather.

In each group someone said, "It's a pity about the candles. It doesn't seem like July Fourth without them."

No one paid any attention to a shadowy figure at the far end of the green.

Suddenly there was a whizzing noise, and out of the blackness came a flash of red light.

The people gasped in wonder. Some were frightened. They thought the world was coming to an end. Some thought the British had come to strike terror into the city. But the brushmaker and Mr. Cossart told of Bob's purchases, and word spread from one group to another.

The sky grew wild with color. Red fire, green fire, yellow fire, and blue fire streamed across the heavens. They made the stars and the moon look small and feeble.

Suddenly from the meetinghouse tower the bells rang out. *Bong! Bong! Bong! Bong!* How the bells rang! How the lights danced!

At last the bells were quiet. The shooting candles, too, had died away.

Now a great huzzah went up from the crowds. There were the deep voices of the men. There were the high voices of the women and children. They mounted until the very earth seemed to tremble from the sound.

Bob laughed. He thought he could hear Abraham's and Polly's voices above all the others.

The applause was deafening. Only Mrs. Fulton stood silent and thankful. But one thing was plain to her: the crowds were cheering not only the second birthday of their country. They were cheering a boy craftsman named Bob Fulton.

Off for
a Holiday

DETER GUMPF, Chris Gumpf's father, took hold of Bob's sleeve and spun him around.

Bob was just entering the wide open doorway of Mr. Messersmith's shop. It was sunup on an April morning in the year 1779. None of the other workmen had arrived. Only Mr. Messersmith was getting ready for the day.

"Look once," said Mr. Gumpf, pointing to the feathery green leaves on the trees. "Spring comes. It is fishing time for Deter Gumpf. You and my boy Chris work hard. I work hard. On Saturday I give you a surprise. I take you boys fishing on Conestoga Creek."

Bob grinned at the thought. Mr. Gumpf was a famous fisherman. Bob had always hoped that someday he would be asked to go along on one of the trips. In his mind's eye he already saw a yellow perch snapping for his bait. Already he dreamed of displaying his large catch of fish to the townspeople when he returned.

Then his eye caught the row of guns. "The guns are still piling up," he said. "Mr. Messersmith may need us."

Mr. Messersmith, who had heard the talk, took two big strides over to Bob.

"Even soldiers get furloughs." He smiled down at the boy. "I give you orders to go fishing on Saturday! You and Chris and Deter Gumpf."

"Oh, sir," exclaimed Bob joyfully, "if you really want us to go! . . ." And he began to sweep out the shop with a light heart.

Saturday was only four days away. But to a boy who liked to fish, it seemed like four years.

CHORES! CHORES! CHORES!

When the day came at last, it turned out to be one of those unexpected hot days that sometimes come in spring.

Bob was up with the first streak of dawn. He flew about his chores. He swept the hearth and stirred the fire. He carried in enough wood to last all day. Quickly he made up a bundle of alder twigs. These he lighted and placed directly inside the brick oven.

The twigs were dry as hay. They began crackling and burning brightly.

Bob shut the heavy iron door.

"There, Matilda," he said to the sleepy cat on the hearth, "if mother likes a hot oven for 'rye-an'-Injun' bread, she shall have a hot oven!"

He poured a little bowl of milk for Matilda and stroked her sleek fur.

"No one would guess," he said, "that you have furnished hair for eighteen brushes!"

Next he ran to the town pump and drew two buckets of drinking water.

When he returned, Mrs. Fulton and the girls were bustling about the kitchen.

Peggy was singing at the top of her lungs:

> "One cup of sweet milk,
> One cup of sour,
> One cup of corn meal,
> One cup of flour,
> Teaspoon of soda,
> Molasses one cup;
> Steam for three hours,
> Then eat it all up."

"Mercy me!" Mrs. Fulton said to Bob. "Have you not been to bed at all? How did you get so much work done this early in the morning?"

She looked about the kitchen with an approving nod. "How tidy everything is! The hearth swept clean. The wood box heaped full. Matilda fed. The water buckets filled. And the oven heating for Saturday's baking."

Bob peeped in the oven. Nothing was left of the twigs but embers and ashes. He swept them into the ashpit. Then he lined the oven with cabbage leaves so the bread would keep clean.

Abraham always managed to come downstairs at this very moment. He liked to shovel the "rye-an'-Injun" loaves into the oven with the long-handled shovel. Then he would turn round and join in the chorus of

"Sleepyhead! Sleepyhead!
Abraham's a sleepyhead!"

Bob was too excited to eat his breakfast. Besides, he was far more interested in the lunch his mother was packing.

First she put in hard-cooked eggs and a tiny package of salt. Then she made corn-bread sandwiches by spreading them with a thick layer of apple butter. She added cookies and doughnuts and a little jug of sweet cider.

When he thought she was finished, she put in the best thing of all—three pieces of fresh rhubarb pie.

"Bob," said Mrs. Fulton, "eat all your oatcakes and drink all your milk. You will have need of a good staying breakfast."

Then in the same breath she called, "Polly, please fetch me a head of cabbage from down cellar. I see cobwebs on the grass. That means the sun will be extraordinarily hot. I shall wrap the sandwiches in cabbage leaves to keep them fresh and moist."

"I think Bob is mean to go off without me," pouted Abraham. "Unless," he giggled, "unless he lets me dig the worms. That's more fun than fishing anyway."

Bob liked to dig worms, too. It was part of the fishing trip. Not quite so good as landing a big fish—but almost! He knew a place near the barn where there were plenty of worms, too.

He was on the point of saying "no" when he looked at his heaping lunch basket and thought of all the fun he would have.

"Yes, you can dig the worms," he said. "But hurry. I don't want to keep Mr. Gumpf waiting, and he always starts early."

Mrs. Fulton's eyes met Bob's with a smile. "I have one more chore for you," she said, "and then you may go. The ashpit is overfull."

The ashpit is overfull!

Bob sighed. Only three or four times a year the ashpit needed emptying. Why did it have to be today?

He shoveled out the ashes as fast as he could, being very careful not to spill any. Ashes were almost as precious as candles. They were used in making soap.

Now the ashpit was empty. Now he could go. He looked about the kitchen quickly. No, he had forgotten none of his chores.

It was nearly two miles to Conestoga Creek, and Bob ran most of the way. His fishing rod made a whipping sound as he ran. The cider in his jug gurgled. Only the worms in the little bucket made no noise at all.

Halfway to the creek Bob met Schoolmaster Caleb Johnson. The schoolmaster eyed the fish pole with disapproval and looked at the lunch basket. "Eat not the bread of idleness!" he said.

Then he noticed Bob's hands, reddened with work. He cleared his throat. "May thy day be rewarded with many fish, Robert!" And he blew his nose and was on his way before Bob could thank him.

When Bob arrived at the meeting place, no one was there. Mr. Gumpf's small flatboat was still padlocked to the trunk of a tree.

Bob stretched out on the bank and mopped his forehead with the back of his sleeve.

For a long time he lay there, listening to the pleasant sound of the water slapping against the boat. The day was growing uncomfortably warm.

Suddenly he heard Chris's whistle and the clanking of Mr. Gumpf's keys.

He sprang to his feet. "Halloo!" he shouted.

Mr. Gumpf could hardly get his key into the padlock, he was so anxious to be off. "Summer comes overnight, yah?" he puffed.

The three fishermen were busy storing their lunches and bait underneath their seats.

Bob let out a great sigh. At last the holiday had begun!

Upstream

THERE WERE NO OARS to Deter Gumpf's boat. Instead there was a long pole with a spike at the end of it.

Mr. Gumpf handed the pole to Bob. "It comes your turn first," he said. "Upstream a little ways is a fine fishing ground. Always the fish are hungry there. Now we see once if Quicksilver Bob can pole a boat quick, like his name." And he laughed a loud laugh.

Bob dug the pole into the bed of the creek and pushed hard. "We're off!" he cried.

The water rippled away on both sides of the boat. The faint stirring of air felt good.

At first, the hard exercise was fun. Bob felt like a conqueror. He enjoyed using his strength to get the best of the current.

By the time he reached the fishing spot, however, all the fun was gone. He was faint with weariness.

Slowly he reached for his bucket of bait. He dug down into the warm mud and pulled out a wriggling worm. He baited his hook.

Slowly he cast his line into the water.

Deter Gumpf took out his flint-and-tinder box and lighted his clay pipe. Then he settled himself to wait for the first nibble.

Chris chewed on a piece of marsh grass and waited for a fish to bite.

Bob felt himself falling asleep.

Suddenly Deter Gumpf was shaking him. "Pull in your line," he called. "We move. I know a better spot. Now it comes Chris's turn to pole the boat."

Chris sighed. "Pa, I'd sooner climb a sapling heels upward. Can't we stay here?"

Deter Gumpf glared at Chris.

Chris argued no further. He threw his weight against the pole. Slowly the boat began to move. They passed tidy farms where hemp and hops were planted in rows as straight as the teeth in a comb. They passed wooded hills with wild cherry trees in bloom.

They traveled so slowly that they could visit with the children who came running to the bank.

Now the shore line became more and more marshy. Willow trees hung over the water.

"Here!" exclaimed Deter Gumpf. "Here it is we catch fish. Whole strings of fish!"

Chris's face was scarlet. He slapped at a mosquito on his forehead.

"Don't make so much noise!" shouted Deter Gumpf. "You boys are as jumpy as corn tassels. How you expect the fish to bite?"

Soon Deter Gumpf's face grew red too—but not from exercise. "The people haf built too many dams," he said angrily. "They are killing the fish." He puffed rapidly at his pipe. "Bob," he said briskly, "we move upstream farther. Again it comes your turn to pole. Stand up! Square your feet! Push!"

Bob dug the pole into the river bottom at a sharp angle. It took all his strength to push the boat out into midstream.

Away from the shade of the willow trees the sun blazed. It pricked Bob's skin like blackberry thorns. It beat down upon the water until the water looked hot. It glared, like a mirror in the sun.

In only a few minutes Bob was drenched in sweat. Sweat dripped from his curly hair. It ran down his face and dripped from his nose and chin. His shirt of coarse linsey-woolsey clung to him damply.

The current seemed to be swifter here. The boat was barely moving. A canoe floated past them, going downstream. The lone fisherman in it laughed and called, "Be ye standing still or be ye going backward?"

No one answered.

The mosquitoes and flies were biting fiercely. They left great lumps on Bob's bare arms. They thrust their daggers through his shirt.

Tiny gnats called midges swarmed over the boat. They got in Bob's eyes, in his ears, down his neck.

To make matters worse, there was the choking smell of Deter Gumpf's pipe. It made Bob feel queer in his stomach.

"Vot a snail's pace!" exploded Deter Gumpf. "Push, boy!"

Bob's arms ached. He wished he were back at the gunsmith shop. The heat of the forge was nothing compared to the midday sun.

He wished the pole would break in two.

He wished he were a horse with a good long tail for switching flies.

He even wished he were in school!

The flatboat grew heavier and clumsier.

He turned to Mr. Gumpf. "Mother sent some fresh rhubarb pie for you," he said breathlessly. "And there's a little jug of cider, too."

Deter Gumpf took his pipe out of his mouth. "Your mother is a fine woman, Bob. A fine woman! When I spy a nice shady spot, then we can eat."

"Pa," spoke up Chris, "I see a good place. It has a rock with picture writing done by the Indians. We could use the rock for a table. It's in the shade, too."

Bob sent a look of thanks to Chris.

"Boys think only of stuffing their stomachs," grumbled Mr. Gumpf. "All right! We eat. We share our lunches."

The rock with the Indian writing did make a fine table, but Bob could not eat. He lay down, dead-tired.

Deter Gumpf, however, had a fine appetite. He liked the looks of Bob's basket better than his own. He went at it greedily. He did not even stop to remove the cabbage leaves in which the sandwiches were wrapped. He ate right through them! Then he washed his food down with great gulps of cider.

Chris ate a piece of rhubarb pie. Then he put his lunch basket over his head to keep off the mosquitoes. Promptly he fell asleep.

BOB ASKS SOME QUESTIONS

When Bob's head stopped pounding, he turned to Mr. Gumpf. "There must be an easier way to move a boat than by poling it, sir," he said.

Mr. Gumpf's stomach was full. He felt good.

"Yah, William Henry thought so, too," he laughed. "He try to find a way."

"You mean William Henry, the gunsmith on Mill Creek?"

"Yah. He had ideas, too. Once he built himself a boat what ran with steam."

Bob forgot his weariness. He sat up straight. "A boat moved by steam," he repeated. "Did it work, sir?" he asked eagerly.

"Ach, it made two—three trips. Then comes a storm. The boat sinks—kerplunk! Like a rock she sinks." Deter Gumpf rammed his fist into the palm of his hand to show how the boat sank.

"That William Henry!" sneered Deter Gumpf. "He thinks too much. Either his nose is stuck in a history book, or he fools with contraptions instead of working."

Bob sharpened a stick with his jackknife. "Here, Mr. Gumpf," he said, "please draw a picture of how the boat worked."

Mr. Gumpf threw the stick into the creek. Then he said in disgust, "It didn't work, I tell you. Anyone knows that boats have to be poled. Some people are always trying to get out of work. Now leave me alone. I come to fish—not to think about moving boats without poling them."

Bob, however, could think of nothing else.

THE WITCH DOCTOR

When Bob reached home, he looked so flushed that his mother felt his head in alarm.

"Is it chills and fever?" asked Abraham hopefully. Abraham liked to play doctor.

Mrs. Fulton nodded.

With the help of all the children, she managed to get Bob upstairs to bed. She put a warming pan at his feet and wrapped him in blankets. She put a poultice of raw onions on his chest. She made him drink dandelion tea.

Bob remembered none of this. The next few days were like a bad dream. His bed seemed to be Deter Gumpf's flatboat, and he was poling, poling, poling—always upstream.

When the fever left, Bob's bad dreams were gone, too. He sat up in bed, enjoying all the attention he was getting. His mother brought him dishes of floating-island pudding, and cooling drinks to keep his fever down. The girls brought him buttercups and wild plum blossoms. Even Matilda brought him her ball of yarn.

Abraham was not to be outdone. One day when all the family were visiting with Bob, Abraham strode into the room with a large bag in his hand.

"I'm a witch doctor!" he announced. "I'm going to make Bob well!"

Then he turned the bag upside down over Bob's bed. Out of it came a hoptoad, two meadow mice, and a garter snake.

The room was in an uproar! Mrs. Fulton and the girls were trying to jump up on the window ledge, on stools, even on the candle shelf!

Polly jumped for the rafters and missed. She landed on Bob's bed, with the hoptoad in her hair. Abraham and Bob laughed until the tears came. Polly was indignant.

"See!" boasted Abraham. "'Twas the hoptoads, the snake, and the meadow mouse that made Bob laugh again. That means he's well."

When all of the little creatures were caught and sent out of doors, Mrs. Fulton sat on the edge of Bob's bed. "Next week you are going away on a little holiday," she said. "And this time it will be a real holiday. A week with Aunt Isabelle in Little Britain Township will build you up."

Paddle Wheels

FROM THE OUTSIDE, Aunt Isabelle's house was not much to look at—just stones, chinked up with lime.

But inside, it was a thing of wonder. The whole loft was a workshop! In it were tools for every job—drills and saws, planes and chisels, a miter box and compasses, hammers, and nails of all sizes.

Aunt Isabelle lived alone. Uncle Joel was in the Army. He had been with General George Washington for three years. And each spring, for three years, Bob had paid Aunt Isabelle a visit. He always enjoyed every minute of it.

"Mind you," said Uncle Joel when he bade Aunt Isabelle good-by, "I want no ruffians using my tools and scattering them about. Some people can never appreciate good tools. But when Robert Fulton comes, he is welcome to all that is in my treasure loft. He will keep my tools in good repair. He will hang each upon its proper peg. The sawed lumber, too, is left for him."

This year Bob went up to the loft almost the minute he arrived at Aunt Isabelle's. He went to work madly. He swept out the cobwebs and sharpened the tools. Then he made sketches of model boats with tiny paddle wheels.

One whole day he spent on the sketches. Then he sawed and chiseled and hammered until it sounded as if forty men were at work.

Aunt Isabelle seemed to understand how important the pounding was. She never complained of the noise. Instead, she visited Bob morning and afternoon.

Always she brought two little mugs of cold milk and a napkin filled with fresh cookies or tarts. One time she brought a blueberry cake.

"What a fine fishing boat!" she exclaimed as she studied his sketches. "I declare! It is so real it makes me a mite seasick." Then she sliced two pieces of the cake and sat down on an upturned keg. "Have a piece of cake, Bob," she said. "Now stop work for a minute and tell me how the boat will work."

No one could make a better cake than Aunt Isabelle. Bob climbed upon the workbench. Between mouthfuls, he explained.

"See these thin blades of wood?"

Aunt Isabelle nodded.

"I aim to fasten them to the spokes of a wheel. Then I will fasten the wheels to a boat, and away she'll go, like a duck paddling upstream. 'Twill be far pleasanter than poling a boat. Did you ever try poling a boat, Aunt Isabelle?"

Aunt Isabelle laughed.

"No, indeed! I've never hankered to pole a boat. I'd fall overboard first thing."

For a whole week Bob worked on the tiny wheels. When at last they were fitted to the boat, he raced down to the creek at the back of the house. With eager hands he placed it in the water. The tiny paddle wheels went round and round. The water churned. The little boat was moving. It was gaining on a fishing boat that had only a pole for its power.

"Why, it's better than wind and sails!" Bob exclaimed.

"She's too big to take home," he told Aunt Isabelle when he left. "Please save it for me until next spring."

"I certainly will save it," Aunt Isabelle promised. "I'll take the best of care of it. Uncle Joel will be interested in seeing it whenever he comes home. He'll be proud of you."

A SURPRISE FOR DETER GUMPF

Back home in Lancaster, Bob went to see Chris at once. He found him in one of the neat barns behind the Gumpf house.

Bob looked around carefully to see that Mr. Gumpf was nowhere within sight.

Then he gave a low whistle.

Chris almost dropped the ox yoke he was hanging on the peg of the barn wall. "Bob!"

"Chris!" Then the two boys suddenly went shy. Finally Chris dived down into his pocket and took out a piece of maple sugar. He divided it and gave half to Bob. Then their tongues flew.

"Chris," began Bob, "we'll never have to pole your Pa's boat again. I made a tiny boat with paddle wheels, and it works."

Big as he was, Chris turned a somersault for joy. Then the two boys sat down behind the barn and laid their plan. They kept their voices low to be sure Mr. Gumpf would not hear them.

First, they agreed that Mr. Gumpf's flatboat must have a pair of paddle wheels at once. Then they agreed that it would have to be a surprise. Mr. Gumpf would never hear of such an idea!

Each night when milking was done, the boys went to work in Bob's barn.

They cut a rod long enough to run through the fishing boat from side to side. Then they bent the rod so that there was a double crank in the middle. Next they made the paddle wheels exactly like those on the model boat.

When at last the wheels were finished, the boys hung them on the wall and stood back to admire their handiwork. They had spent many hours on the project and were satisfied with the result.

"They look like the letter X," exclaimed Chris.

"The letter X with webfeet," laughed Bob.

Now the boys faced a real problem. How were they to fasten the wheels onto the boat without Deter Gumpf knowing about it?

It was Mr. Messersmith who solved the problem. He needed a load of charcoal. He asked Mr. Gumpf if Chris and Bob could go up to Rockford and fetch the charcoal in the little flatboat.

While Deter Gumpf was taking the key to the padlock off his chain, Bob winked at Mr. Messersmith. "If we are gone overlong," he said, "don't fret. Chris and I have a surprise. It will soon make up for all the lost time."

Chris and Bob hurried to their workshop. Each picked up one of the wheels. Then Chris, being the bigger, took the long rod. Bob took a sack of tools and a small hand paddle which he had made in secret.

What a sight they made as they raced for the creek, carrying the big wheels. Chickens fluttered out of their way. Pigs squealed and dogs barked. Cats ran up trees. People poked their heads outside to see what caused the excitement.

Women going to market hopped aside quickly as soon as they saw the contraptions. They did not want to risk having their starched caps lifted off their heads by wooden blades that looked like butter paddles.

Children shouted at Bob: "Halloo there, Quicksilver! Be you and Chris using windmills so's you can run faster?"

At last Chris was fitting the key into the padlock. At last the moment had come!

With fast-beating heart, Bob bored two holes on opposite sides of the boat, near the top rail. Then he fitted the long rod into the holes. It stuck out about six inches on both sides.

Bob gave a cry of joy when he found that the rod was just long enough to hold the wheels. While Chris fastened the paddle wheels onto the ends of the rod, Bob drilled a hole in the stern for the hand paddle.

"Now turn the crank, Chris," said Bob.

"No, you turn it, Bob."

Bob's fingers ached to try it himself. But this was Mr. Gumpf's boat. "It is your father's boat, Chris. You should be the one to try it."

Chris turned the crank. There was a splashing of wheels. "She goes ahead all right!" he shouted. "But how shall we guide her?"

Chris looked so puzzled Bob could not help laughing. Guiding the boat was no problem to the young inventor.

For the answer he fitted the hand paddle into the hole in the stern. Now while Chris turned the crank, Bob steered the boat with the paddle.

The boys let out a great war whoop as they splashed their way up to Conestoga Creek at two miles an hour.

Even when the load of charcoal was taken on, the boat traveled along as merry as a breeze. She traveled so fast going downstream that the ducks on the water flew away with a noisy clatter. People on the bank looked at the amazing contraption with open-mouthed wonder.

"Look!" cried Chris. "Look! There's Pa waiting for us on the bank."

Bob had never seen Mr. Gumpf so excited. He was running back and forth, his arms making wild signals.

"Ho-ho!" laughed Chris. "He reminds me of a hen that hatched out a duck and is afeared it will drown!"

Bob never forgot that summer. Fishing days were fun now. But as much as Bob liked to fish, he had discovered something important. The making of the paddle wheels had been more exciting than all the fishing trips in the world!

Bob Meets Benjamin Franklin

A HEAVY FOG lay over the city of Lancaster. It was four o'clock on a raw November morning in 1782.

The houses were still barred and shuttered. The street lanterns were still burning dimly. They looked like sleepy, one-eyed monsters.

The Fulton family felt their way along in the fog. Now they touched a familiar fence. Now a tree. Yes, they were on the lane that led to the inn, but they had to go very slowly. They frequently called to one another to be sure that nobody was lost. They had not been outside very long, but they were already damp and cold.

In an hour the stagecoach would be leaving. In an hour it would be taking a seventeen-year-old boy to Philadelphia, the capital of the United States. In an hour Bob Fulton, the boy, would belong to the world of men. He would be on his way to seek his fortune in the largest city in all of the thirteen states.

Bob did not feel man-grown, however. He had a queer empty feeling at the pit of his stomach. Even his voice had a hollow sound as he told his mother not to worry.

Abraham was breathing hard. He insisted on carrying Bob's green satchel, although it was entirely filled and very heavy.

Peggy and Belle and Polly were as silent as the fog. Each of them was trying not to cry.

Suddenly there was a rumbling sound, and the clatter of hoofs. Only the stagecoach with its four-horse team could possibly make that much noise. It must be leaving early!

Bob took his satchel from Abraham and began running. The family was running, too.

Breathless, they reached the inn. The passengers were climbing aboard. They were trying to find room for trunks and bundles of every description. The driver was shouting in a loud voice: "Are ye all aboard?"

Now Peggy was pressing something into Bob's hand. "I made you a cake of bayberry soap," she shouted above the din.

Mrs. Fulton put her lips close to Bob's ear. "Here are your journey cakes," she said with a catch in her voice. "They are golden brown—the way you like them. Good-by, my big brave son! My big brave son . . ."

Again the shout: "Are ye all aboard?"

Bob leaped up on the seat next to the driver. He longed to gather the whole family into his arms. Yet he was half glad there was no time to say good-by.

It seemed as if part of him had already gone on ahead to Philadelphia. The other part of him seemed back in Lancaster, carrying in firewood and laughing with the family.

There was a loud cry for the horses. The driver cracked the whip, and the stagecoach rumbled off into the blackness of the morning. When Bob tried to look out through the darkness and the fog, he could see nothing.

PEPPER POT

Bob stepped briskly along High Street in Philadelphia. Under his arm he carried a large portfolio. He was in high spirits. He had *four* drawings to deliver this morning!

There was the carriage design for the factory, the signboard for the inn, the drawing for the machine shop, and the miniature for a family named Gage.

Three years had elapsed since Bob left Lancaster. Three whole years. Sometimes he had gone hungry. Sometimes he had worked late at night until his fingers were blue with cold.

But this morning all the hunger and the struggles were forgotten.

He hummed a little tune under his breath. He was thinking that now he could walk into the office of the city director and say, "Kindly put in your directory:

> 'Robert Fulton, painter of miniatures
> Corner 2d and Walnut Streets'"

Bob was so busy with his thoughts that he did not see the big Negro woman coming toward him with her two-wheeled soup cart.

Nor did he notice an old gentleman coming along behind the woman.

Suddenly a gust of wind lifted Bob's hat. It went skimming upward like a kite.

Without thinking, he made a wild leap after it. The next thing he knew, the cart was wrong side up. The soup woman had gone bouncing into the arms of the old gentleman. Bob himself sprawled ungracefully over the cart.

All up and down High Street, window shutters flew open. Heads popped out. Bob felt as if a thousand eyes were on him and the overturned cart.

Soup was spilled everywhere. Bob was covered with it. The pepper-pot-soup woman was covered with it. The old gentleman's black suit was dotted with thick blobs of it.

Only the portfolio had escaped.

The air was filled with the steaming fragrance of beef and onions and herbs.

"Oh, my pepper-pot soup! Oh, my good pepper-pot soup!" wailed the woman.

"I'm sorry," Bob stammered. "I'll manage to pay for your soup. Somehow I'll manage."

Then he turned to the gentleman. "My name, sir, is Robert Fulton. I cannot pay for your suit just now. But, sir, I could paint your portrait."

And then Bob clapped his hand to his head.

"Why, why," he gasped, "you are Benjamin Franklin! I didn't look at you closely, sir, or I would have recognized you."

The kindly old gentleman finished wiping the soup from his square-rimmed spectacles. He did not seem greatly disturbed by the incident.

"I propose," he said with a little smile, "that you bring your easel and your paintbox to my home this evening at seven. It is some time since I had a good portrait. Now I must be on my way.

"Oh, Mr. Fulton," he added, "be so good as to bring some of your sketches with you. I should like very much to see them."

"*Mr.* Fulton!" whispered Bob. "Why, no one has ever called me that before!" And he strode along unmindful of his spattered suit.

Bob walked up the three steps to the Franklin home. His heart thumped wildly.

Suppose the great Dr. Franklin did not like his work! Suppose he had a roomful of callers! Suppose he had forgotten about his promise!

Before Bob could pull the bell rope, the plump old gentleman had thrown the door wide open. "Come in, young man," he said. "I have been looking forward to your visit."

In no time at all, Bob's easel was set up in the cozy parlor, and he and the greatest man in Philadelphia were visiting like old friends. Bob explained how he had come to Philadelphia for new opportunities and what he had been doing since he had arrived.

Bob showed Dr. Franklin his designs and sketches. Dr. Franklin showed Bob his old wooden hand press, the first Franklin stove, and one of the first Franklin pennies.

"Do you know," said Benjamin Franklin with a twinkle in his eye, "you and I are alike in many ways. I, too, came to Philadelphia when I was seventeen years old. And we are both interested in making things."

Bob had to work swiftly. Dr. Franklin was a lively man. He did not sit still for very long at a time. Every now and again he took a quick turn about the room.

Now he stopped before the easel. The few strokes were rough and unfinished. But already the likeness to his own plump self was very plain.

"Why, lad," he exclaimed, "you are a second Benjamin West!"

Then he stood looking at the boy. "How would you like to study under Benjamin West?" he asked suddenly.

Bob's hand trembled. "How would I like to study under Benjamin West!" he breathed. Just thinking about it gave him goose flesh.

"You know," Dr. Franklin went on, "I went to London to improve myself as a printer. I think one day you will go to London, too. Benjamin West could instruct you in his art. He could also introduce you to men of science. You would benefit by their wisdom. I shall write a letter to West, telling him about your talents. I think he would be interested in you."

Bob stopped his work. He did not want to miss a single word. He could see new horizons. Having enough work and getting his name in the city directory did not seem very important.

"I shall tell him that you are a craftsman as well as an artist. And I make no doubt of it that he and his kind wife Elizabeth will take you under their wing."

Dr. Franklin sat down at his desk and reached for his quill pen. Bob went on with his work.

The man and the boy were silent. The only sound was made by the scratching of the quill.

Now Dr. Franklin was signing the letter. Bob could hear the pen strokes winding in and out as they formed the letters:

Just as Dr. Franklin blotted the letter with sand, a maidservant entered the room. And of all things, she brought in two steaming bowls of pepper-pot soup.

How Benjamin Franklin and Bob laughed!

"I declare!" chuckled Dr. Franklin, "I shall never see a bowl of pepper-pot again without thinking of Robert Fulton."

Off to Europe

WHEN BOB WAS fired with an idea, he could not rest until he had worked it out. Although he had been seriously ill for part of that year and had not yet recovered, he began to make plans to go to England immediately.

He wanted to be a great artist like Benjamin West, and he wanted to begin his training without any further delay.

First he had to take care of his mother and his sisters. After consulting them, he bought a farm where they could live. He spent nearly all the money he had saved during the time he had been in Philadelphia to pay for the farm.

He finished all the work he had on hand. In 1787 he sailed for England, carrying letters of introduction to many important people in Europe. He was especially pleased to have a letter from Benjamin Franklin to Benjamin West.

As soon as Bob reached London, he got in touch with the famous artist. Mr. West, who was now one of the most fashionable painters in London, received his young countryman kindly. Soon the two artists became close friends.

At this time Bob's chief ambition was to learn all he could from this great artist. He began his studies with enthusiasm and was delighted to accept the invitation of this kind man to live in his home.

Mr. West was acquainted with a great many prominent people, and he introduced most of them to Bob. The young man met not only artists and people who wanted their portraits painted, but also many other influential people.

Bob should have been satisfied, but his active mind soon demanded something more. He decided to take a tour of English castles and study some of the fine paintings which they contained. He planned to copy some of the pictures which he admired most in an effort to improve his work.

He went to Devon, intending to paint some of the scenery there. He had not been in that part of the country long when he became interested in a canal on which a large amount of coal was being transported. He discovered that this canal, and several others, were carrying coal to Manchester, an important manufacturing town.

He learned that many of these canals were on the estate of the Duke of Bridgewater. The Duke had built these canals to carry coal from mines on his estate. Bob forgot about his painting as soon as he saw this ingenious means of transportation. He wanted to meet the man who had devised it, and before long he had the opportunity.

The Duke of Bridgewater was now planning to extend his system of canals to the sea and to some other cities. He recognized in Robert Fulton a man who could be useful in this work. He hired Bob to go to Birmingham, where much of the Duke's coal was sent, to study plans for building more canals. Bob stayed there eighteen months, and he met many scientists and engineers.

He became more and more interested in the development of the canals. One day when he was looking at them, a new idea came to him. He spent the whole night working out a rough drawing of a device to raise and lower the canal boats. At a later date he secured a patent from the British government for this invention.

He was always interested in finding ways to do work more quickly and easily. He invented a machine for digging channels for the canals, a boat that would carry the goods faster, and devices for spinning flax and making rope.

By this time Robert Fulton was greatly interested in the French Revolution. This was a war in which King Louis XVI lost his throne and the country became a republic. Bob had not forgotten the American Revolution, which had happened during his boyhood. His sympathies were with the French people, who had been misruled. Finally he went to Paris.

While he was living in France, he invented the first submarine torpedo-boat. He named this ship the "Nautilus." He offered this submarine to the French government, but it was never used. The British, who were fighting against the French, were sufficiently alarmed to consider purchasing it, but did not do so.

Also, the British and the Americans were disagreeing at this time, and Robert Fulton realized the danger of war between the two countries. He did not want the submarine torpedo-boat to be used against his own country.

At this time Robert Fulton had been away from the United States for twenty years. During all these years he had been studying physics, chemistry, and mathematics. He had been constantly experimenting and acquiring practical knowledge. He had invented a number of complicated machines during this period.

For many years a number of people in England, France, and the United States had been attempting to build a practical steamboat. There were many problems to be overcome before such a boat could be made to work. Various inventors had suggested ideas. Some had made models, and an Englishman and a Frenchman had actually built steamboats. Neither boat worked.

Robert Fulton had followed all these experiments with interest. In 1802 he formed a partnership with Robert R. Livingston wherein the two men agreed to attempt to build a steamboat that could be operated successfully.

Late in 1806 Mr. Fulton returned to America. He devoted the winter and most of the next summer to building and perfecting his steamboat, which he named the "Clermont." While the boat was being built, a group of unemployed men congregated nearby and poked fun at the project. They called it "Fulton's Folly." The inventor had to hire guards to protect his boat against these men and against sloops that nearly rammed and wrecked it.

Robert Fulton, Steamboat Builder

THE YEARS had gone by. Things worked out pretty much as Benjamin Franklin said they would.

Robert Fulton had gone to London. He had been taken under the wing of Benjamin West. He had been given lessons in art and introduced to men of science—both in England and France. He had many important friends.

Now Robert Fulton had come back home to America. He was Mr. Fulton now. But Mr. Fulton, at forty-one, still looked ahead, eagerly. He was still slender and dark-haired. And he stood well over six feet.

It was just past noon in New York City. The date was August 17, 1807. The day was fair. A light breeze was stirring. The North River glistened in the sun.

All morning a curious crowd had been gathering at the wharf—small boys with their fishing rods, young men and old men, workers and loafers. A great many people even stood on the housetops on the hill. It was a restless crowd that seemed to be waiting for something.

All eyes were looking down at a strange boat tied to the dock. It had masts like any ordinary sailboat. But between her masts, there was an array of machinery and a tall smokestack! And fastened to her sides were paddle wheels! The name "Clermont" was painted on her hull.

The watchers on the wharf and on the housetops were not silent. Some were laughing. "That snub-nosed little steamboat!" they were saying. "It will sink before it reaches Albany."

"Course it will," someone answered. "Who wants to travel in a boat driven by a tea kettle? Sailboats were good enough for our fathers. They're good enough for us."

More than one person wagged his head and said, "I'm glad it isn't any of my money going to be sunk with the 'Clermont.' I feel sorry for that Fulton fellow. I understand he's worked on the idea of a steamboat for years."

"The fellow *I* feel sorry for is Chancellor Livingston," said an old man. "It's Livingston's money that paid for the ugly duckling. Just naming the boat 'Clermont' for his country home isn't going to be much honor when the boat blows to bits. I hear Livingston has refused to sink any more money in 'Fulton's folly.'"

"You're right, grandpap!" laughed a sun-browned fisherman. "Even Livingston pokes fun at it. Says it looks like a sawmill mounted on a scow and set on fire!"

"Look!" cried a little boy. "They're giving the signal to start! The Clermont is ready for its first run from New York to Albany!"

Pfft! Chug, chug! The engine roared above the voices. The smokestack spit fire and smoke. The paddle wheels turned. The boat snorted away from the dock!

The crowd on the wharf and on the housetops waited for something to happen.

Would the machinery be too heavy for the boat? Would the boat sink as soon as it started moving up the river?

Would the boiler explode?

Would the passengers be tossed skyward?

And then the air was filled with laughter, loud laughter. Even Mr. Fulton's friends shrugged.

The steamboat had stopped dead! The paddle wheels were still. Once again the water was as smooth as a mill pond.

"What did we tell you!" the crowd mocked.

"Hush!" exclaimed one of the watchers. "Mr. Fulton is standing up on a platform."

"What's he saying? What's he saying?" asked the people on the housetops.

"He's asking the passengers to be patient," shouted a man near the boat.

"Ho, ho!" laughed the crowd. " 'Twill take more than patience! Toss the smokestack and boiler overboard! Hoist the sails!"

Suddenly the laughter stopped short. Once more the boat was leaving the dock. It was moving against the wind. It was moving against the tide. The watchers could not believe it.

It was passing flatboats and sailboats as if they were at anchor! Some of them headed for shore, like frightened children running home to mother. Some of the sailors jumped from their boats into the water and swam to shore.

"She's bewitched!" shrieked an old woman high on a housetop.

Many people thought the Clermont looked like a monster. When they saw smoke and sparks coming from the boat, they thought it was on fire. A few thought it was a monster, breathing fire.

"She sails! She sails! She sails!"

"Hooray for the 'Clermont!'"

"Hooray for Fulton!"

BINDING THE STATES TOGETHER

The United States flag was flying over Mr. Messersmith's shop. It flew proudly—almost as if it knew the importance of the day.

Inside, the shop was alive with townspeople. It seemed as if all Lancaster was trying to crowd in.

Mr. Messersmith stood near the doorway, greeting the people. His hands trembled, not only because he was old. They trembled because he was so excited, too.

He was wearing a new suit. His apron hung upon its peg. There was no fire in the forge. No ox was in the ox cage. No horses were tied to the hitching post. The shop was as clean as a kitchen, and just as neat.

Hans Holzer, the Swiss settler, was in the crowd. Schoolmaster Caleb Johnson was there, too, and Mr. Cossart, the little old storekeeper.

Mr. Holzer was studying a newspaper clipping tacked up over the workbench.

When he turned away, he had to dry off his spectacles. Then he wiped his eyes.

"It gives a good feeling," he sighed happily, "to know even more than this newspaper says. Sure, the 'Clermont' begins a new era in transportation. Sure, it goes a hundred and fifty miles in thirty-two hours. But that is not the whole story. The newspaperman says nothing about the canals. I, Hans Holzer, say the real story is in the canals. Eh, Mr. Johnson?"

"How is that?" asked Mr. Johnson.

"You remember how Bob was late to school when he watched me dig my canal, yah?"

Master Johnson started to speak, but Mr. Holzer went right on.

"Only a month ago Bob said to me, 'Hans Holzer, soon the United States will be tied together by canals! Your hemp and hops will go to market by water, Hans. Soon canals and steamboats bind the whole country together!'"

Now Mr. Holzer was pounding the workbench in excitement. "'Hans,' he say to me, 'Philadelphia and Lake Erie could be joined by a canal!'"

"Ach!" sputtered Mr. Holzer, as he threw up his hands in disgust. "This clipping says only half, eh, schoolmaster?"

"Thou hast well spoken," replied Caleb Johnson. "The newspaper tells only half. How many of thee remember Robert's twenty-first birthday?

"How many of thee remember that he expected no birthday remembrances from his mother? Instead, with his savings, he bought her a farm in Washington County."

"That's so!" shouted a young man. "He even bought lots nearby for Peggy and Belle and Polly and Abraham."

"What about all his inventions?" asked a man on the edge of the crowd. "The newspaper says nothing about them!"

"Yes!" chorused the men.

"He invented a machine for spinning flax," said one. "It worked, too."

"And a machine for making rope!" said another. "We could finish in half the time."

"And a mill for sawing marble!" said someone else. "The marble didn't break, either."

"I have a gun he designed," said an old man. "I used it during the war, and it's still just as good as it ever was."

"Yah," spoke up Mr. Holzer again, "don't forget his power shovels for digging canals. Always he wanted to find quicker and better ways of doing things."

"He built a boat to go under water, too!" an old man reminded the crowd.

Now Mr. Cossart, the little storekeeper, was making his way up to the workbench. He had been eagerly waiting his turn. He wanted to tell his story, too.

"*I* think," he said in his high squeaky voice, "*I* think the paper forgets that Bob is an artist. Why, his pictures were exhibited in the Royal Academy! And it was his drawings that served him whilst he built the steamboat!"

The preacher, too, had a word to say. "Know ye," his voice boomed forth, "that just four years ago, in Paris, Robert Fulton builded another boat upon the Seine River. It was ready for its trial trip. Know ye what happened?"

"What?" cried the men.

"One day it lay afloat upon the water awaiting its trial trip. A windstorm came up. Lo, the ship cracked open like the shell of an egg. The engine sank to the bottom of the Seine."

"Oh!" breathed the listeners.

"But, my brethren, did Robert Fulton wail? Nay. He went amongst the workmen. He dived into the icy waters. He inspired the men. And behold, in twenty-four hours the engine was again above the water, and later a second boat was builded."

"Did it work?" asked a small boy.

"Aye. The people praised it. But Robert Fulton knew it could be made better. He wrote to Mr. Watt of England. He ordered a steam engine to be builded and sent to America. That engine, my brethren, furnished the power for the 'Clermont.'"

All this while, the gunsmith had stood silent.

Now he took a small cowhide apron from a peg on the wall. With shaking hands, he held it up proudly, and looked from one friendly face to another.

"I love Bob," he smiled. "I have always kept his apron because it reminded me of him. How proud he was when the new look began to wear off of it! Why, it's still rounded out as if Bob were inside it!" he said softly.

Mr. Messersmith let out a great sigh. He mopped his brow. He was not used to making speeches, and he was embarrassed.

But the crowd waited. It was plain that the gunsmith had more to say.

"Others there were," he said at last, "who had ideas about moving boats by steam. But Bob went on from where they left off. Even as a boy he was the kind to see a way to improve things. He always finished up whatever he set out to do, too, and he made a fine job of it."

Then the gunsmith chuckled. "Bob was never happy unless he was making something — something according to a plan. And if he had two or three plans, he was two or three times as happy. He'd often be working on all three plans at one time, and he'd be drawing plans for more projects before others were completed."

"Whoever dreamed," he said in a whisper, "that the boy who used to work in my shop would one day build a steamboat, and that his steamboat would bind states together?"